The Life Of The Scorpion

by

J. Henri Fabre

Double 9 BOOKS

The Life Of The Scorpion

by J. Henri Fabre

ISBN: 978-93-71814-89-8

Published by

DOUBLE 9 BOOKS

2/13-B, Ansari Road
Daryaganj, New Delhi – 110002
info@double9books.com
www.double9books.com
Tel. 011-40042856

ABOUT THE AUTHOR

Jean-Henri Casimir Fabre was a French naturalist and entomologist celebrated for his engaging writings on insect life. Born to Antoine Fabre and Victoire Salgues in Saint-Léons, France, he developed a profound interest in nature and the behaviors of insects that shaped his career. Fabre's work combined scientific observation with a lively narrative style that brought the natural world to life for readers. Throughout his life, he remained dedicated to exploring and documenting the complexities of insect behavior, particularly beetles and other small creatures. His contributions significantly influenced popular science literature and entomology, making the study of insects accessible and fascinating to a broader audience. Fabre was married twice, first to Marie-Césarine Villard and later to Marie Joséphine Daudel, and had a son named Paul-Henri Fabre. He lived a long life, passing away at the age of 91 in Sérignan-du-Comtat, France. His legacy continues through his detailed observations and writings that highlight the intricate and often overlooked aspects of insect life.

CONTENTS

CHAPTER I
THE LANGUEDOCIAN SCORPION: THE DWELLING

The Scorpion is an uncommunicative creature, secret in his practices and disagreeable to deal with, so that his history, apart from anatomical detail, amounts to little or nothing. The scalpel of the experts has made us acquainted with his organic structure; but no observer, as far as I know, has thought of interviewing him, with any sort of persistence, on the subject of his private habits. Ripped up, after being steeped in spirits of wine, he is very well-known; acting within the domain of his instincts, he is hardly known at all. And yet none of the segmented animals is more deserving of a detailed biography. He has at all times appealed to the popular imagination, even to the point of figuring among the signs of the zodiac. Fear made the gods, said Lucretius. Deified by terror, the Scorpion is immortalized in the sky by a constellation and in the almanac by the symbol for the month of October.

I made the acquaintance of the Languedocian Scorpion (*Scorpio occitanus*, LAT) half a century ago, in the Villeneuve hills, on the far side of the Rhone, opposite Avignon. When the thrice-blessed Thursday1 came, from morning till night I used to turn over the stones in quest of the Scolopendra,2 the chief subject of the thesis which I was preparing for my doctor's degree. Sometimes, instead of that magnificent horror, the mighty Myriapod, I would find, under the raised stone, another and no less unpleasant recluse. It was he. With his tail turned over his back and a drop of poison gleaming at the end of the sting, he lay displaying his pincers at the entrance to a burrow. Br-r-r-r! Have done with the formidable creature! The stone fell back into its place.

Utterly tired out, I used to return from my excursions rich in Scolopendræ and richer still in those illusions which paint the future rose-colour when we first begin to bite freely into the bread of knowledge. Science! The witch! I used to come home with joy in my heart: I had found some Centipedes. What more was needed to complete my ingenuous happiness? I carried off the Scolopendræ and left the Scorpions behind, not without a secret feeling that a day would come when I should have to concern myself with them.

Fifty years have elapsed; and that day has come. It behoves me, after the Spiders,3 his near neighbours in organization, to cross-examine my old acquaintance, chief of the Arachnids in our district. It so happens that the Languedocian Scorpion abounds in my neighbourhood; nowhere have I seen him so plentiful as on the Sérignan hills, with their sunny, rocky slopes beloved by the arbutus and the arborescent heath. There the chilly creature finds a sub-tropical temperature and also a sandy soil, easy to dig. This is, I think, as far as he goes towards the north.

His favourite spots are the bare expanses poor in vegetation, where the rock, outcropping in vertical strata, is baked by the sun and worn by the wind and rain until it ends by crumbling into flakes. He is usually found in colonies at quite a distance from one another, as though the members of a single family, migrating in all directions, were becoming a tribe. It is not sociability, it is anything but that. Excessively intolerant and passionately devoted to solitude, they continually occupy their shelters alone. In vain do I seek them out: I never find two of them under the same stone; or, to be more accurate, when there are two, one is engaged in eating the other. We shall have occasion to see the savage hermit ending the nuptial festivities in this fashion.

The lodging is very rough and ready. Let us turn over the stones, which are generally flat and fairly large. The Scorpion's presence is indicated by a cavity as wide as the neck of a quart bottle and a few inches deep. In stooping, we commonly see the master of the house on the threshold of his dwelling, with his pincers outspread and his tail in the posture of defence. At other times, when he owns a deeper cell, the hermit is invisible. We have to use a small pocket-trowel to bring him out into the light of day. Here he is, lifting or brandishing his weapon. 'Ware fingers!

I take him by the tail with a pair of tweezers and slip him, head foremost, into a stout paper bag, which will isolate him from the other prisoners. The whole of my formidable harvest goes into a tin box. In this way both the collecting and the transport are carried out with perfect safety.

Before housing my animals, let me briefly describe them. The common Black Scorpion (*Scorpio europæus*, LINN.) is known to all. He frequents the dark holes and corners near our dwelling-places; on rainy days in autumn he makes his way indoors, sometimes even under our bed-clothes. The odious animal causes us more fright than damage. Although not rare in my present abode, the results of its visits are never in the least serious. The weird beast, overrated in reputation, is repulsive rather than dangerous.

Much more to be feared and much less well-known generally is the Languedocian Scorpion, resident in the Mediterranean provinces. Far from seeking our habitations, he lives apart, in the untilled solitudes. Beside the Black Scorpion he is a giant who, when full-grown, measures three to three and a half inches in length. His colouring is the yellow of faded straw.

The tail, which is really the animal's abdomen, is a series of five prismatic segments, shaped like little kegs whose staves meet in undulating ridges resembling strings of beads. Similar cords cover the arms and fore-arms of the nippers and divide them into long facets. Others meander along the back like the joints of a cuirass whose seams are adorned with a freakish milled edging. These bead-like protuberances give the Scorpion's armour a fierce and robustious appearance which is characteristic of the Languedocian Scorpion. It is as though the animal were fashioned out of chips hewn with an adze.

The tail ends in a sixth joint, which is smooth and vesicular. This is the gourd in which the poison, a formidable fluid resembling water in appearance, is elaborated and held in reserve. A dark, curved and very sharp sting completes the apparatus. A pore, visible only under the lens, opens at some distance from the point. Through this the venomous liquid is injected into the puncture. The sting is very hard and very sharp. Holding it between my finger-tips, I can push it through a sheet of cardboard as easily as if I were using a needle.

Owing to its bold curve, the sting points downwards when the tail is extended in a straight line. To make use of his weapon, therefore, the Scorpion must raise it, turn it over and strike upwards. This, in fact, is his invariable practice. In order to pink the adversary subdued by the nippers, the tail is arched over the animal's back and brought forward. The Scorpion, for that matter, is almost always in this position: whether in motion or at rest, he arches his tail over his back. He very rarely drags it behind him, relaxed into a straight line.

The pincers, those buccal hands recalling the claws of the Crayfish, are organs of battle and of information. When moving forwards, the Scorpion holds them in front of him, with the two fingers opened, to take stock of objects encountered on the way. When he wants to stab an enemy, the pincers seize the foe and hold him motionless, while the sting is brought into play over the assailant's back. Lastly, when he wishes to nibble a tit-bit at leisure, they serve as hands and hold the prey within the reach of the mouth. They are never used for walking, for stability or for excavation.

That is the function of the real legs. These are suddenly truncated and end in a group of short, movable claws, faced by a short, fine point, which, to some extent, serves as a thumb. The stump is finished off with rough bristles. The whole constitutes an excellent grapnel, which explains the

Scorpion's aptitude for roaming over the trellis-work of my wire-gauze covers, for making long halts there, motionless and upside down, and, lastly, for scrambling along a vertical wall, notwithstanding his clumsiness and weight.

Underneath, just behind the legs, are the combs, those strange organs, an exclusive attribute of the Scorpions. They owe their name to their structure, consisting of a long row of plates, set close together like the teeth of a hair-comb. The anatomists are inclined to ascribe to them the functions of a clutch intended to hold the couple bound together at the moment of pairing. We will leave it at that until we are better informed, provided that the specimens which I propose to rear tell me their secret.

On the other hand, I know of another function, which is very easily observed when the Scorpion meanders, belly uppermost, over the wire trellis of my dish-covers. When he is at rest, the two combs are laid flat on the abdomen, behind the legs. The moment he begins to walk, they stick out on either side, at right angles to the body, like the naked wings of an unfledged nestling. They sway gently up and down, reminding us of the balancing-pole of an inexperienced rope-dancer.4 If the Scorpion stops, they are at once retracted, fall back upon the belly and cease to move: if he resumes his walk, they are at once extended and again begin their gentle oscillation. The animal therefore seems to use them at least as a balancing mechanism.

The eyes, eight in number, are divided into three groups. In the middle of that weird segment which is at once head and thorax, two large and very convex eyes gleam side by side, reminding us of the Lycosa's5 superb lenses; they are apparently in both instances for use at close range, because of their great convexity. A ridge of protuberances arranged in a wavy line serves as an eyebrow and gives them a fierce appearance. Their axis, which is almost horizontal, can hardly allow them more than lateral vision.

The same remark applies to two other groups, each composed of three eyes, which are very small and placed much farther forward, nearly on the edge of the sudden truncation that forms an arch above the mouth. On both right and left the three tiny lenses are set in a short straight line, their axis pointing laterally. On the whole, both the small and the large eyes are so arranged that it can by no means be easy for the animal to obtain a clear view ahead.

Extremely short-sighted and squinting outrageously, how does the Scorpion manage to steer himself? Like a blind man, he gropes his way: he guides himself with his hands, that is to say, his pincers, which he carries outstretched, with the fingers open, to sound the space before him. Watch two Scorpions wandering in the open air in my rearing-cages. A meeting would be disagreeable, sometimes even dangerous for them. Nevertheless, the one behind always goes ahead as though he did not perceive his neighbour; but, as soon as he touches the other ever so little with his pincers, he at once gives a sudden start, a sign of surprise and uneasiness, followed at once by a retreat and a change of direction. To recognize the irascible one thus overhauled, he had to touch him.

Let us now instal our prisoners. I shall never learn all I want to know by turning over stones and making chance observations on the adjacent hills: I must resort to keeping the animals in captivity, the only manner of inducing them to reveal their domestic habits. What rearing-method shall I employ? One in particular appeals to me, one which will leave the creature its full liberty, which will relieve me of the cares of catering and which will enable me to inspect my captives at any hour of the day, from year's end to year's end. This seems to me an excellent means, far superior to the others, so much so that I reckon on a magnificent success.

It is a question of establishing within my own grounds, in the open air, a hamlet of Scorpions, by cunning securing for them the same conditions of well-being which they enjoyed at home. In the first days of January, I found my colony right at the end of the *harmas*,6 in the quiet corner exposed to the sun and sheltered from the north wind by a thick rosemary-hedge. The ground, a mixture of pebbles and red clayey soil, is unsuitable. Considering the temperament of my charges, great stay-at-homes from what I can see, this is easily remedied. For each of my colonists I dig a hole, of a gallon or two in capacity, and fill it with sandy earth similar to that of the original site. I pack this earth lightly, which will give it the consistence needed for digging without land-slips, and in it I contrived a short entrance-passage, the beginning of the excavation which the Scorpion will not fail to make in order to obtain a cell in conformity with his tastes. A wide flat stone covers and overlaps the whole. Opposite the passage of my own making, I scoop out a hollow: this is the entrance-door.

In front of the hollow I place a Scorpion, taken that moment from the paper bag in which he has just been conveyed from the mountain. Seeing a retreat similar to those with which he is familiar, he goes in of his own accord and does not show himself again. In this way I establish the hamlet, consisting of some twenty inhabitants, all adults. The dwellings, placed at a suitable distance from one another, to avoid the quarrels liable to occur among neighbours, are arranged in a row on a stretch of ground cleared with the rake. It will be easy for me to observe events at a glance, even at night, by the light of a lantern. As to food, I need not trouble about that. My guests will find their own provisions, for the spot is quite as well-stocked with game as that from which I brought them.

The colonies in the paddock are not enough. Certain observations call for minute attention which is incompatible with the disturbances out of doors. A second menagerie is set up, this time on the large table in my study, a table around which I have already covered and am still covering so many miles in pursuit of stubborn knowledge. Bring up the big earthenware pans, my usual apparatus! Filled with sifted sandy earth, each receives two broad potsherds, which, half buried, form a ceiling and represent the refuge under the stones. The establishment is surrounded by the dome of a wire-gauze cover.

Here I house the Scorpions, two by two and of different sexes, as far as I am able to judge. No outward characteristic that I know of distinguishes the males from the females. I take the big bellied specimens for females and the less obese for males. As age intervenes with its variations of stoutness, mistakes are inevitable, unless I first open the subject's paunch, a procedure which would cut short any attempt at rearing. We will allow ourselves to be guided by size, since we have no other means of judging, and house the Scorpions two by two, one corpulent and brown, the other less obese and of a lighter colour. There are certain to be some actual couples among the number.

Here are a few details for the benefit of whoso may care one day to take up similar studies. An animal-breeder's trade calls for apprenticeship; the experience of others is not unhelpful, especially when the animals in question are dangerous to deal with. It would never do inadvertently to lay a hand on one of my present prisoners who had escaped from his cage and lay skulking among the utensils littering the table. Serious precautions must be taken by those who propose to spend whole years in the company of such neighbours. They are as follows:

The trellis-work dome is fitted deep into the pan and touches the earthenware bottom. Between the two there is a circular space which I fill with clay soil, packed while wet. So fitted, the wire cover is quite immovable; the apparatus runs no risk of coming to pieces and yielding a way of escape. On the other hand, if the Scorpions dig deeply on the edges of the earthy space at their disposal, they come upon either the wire-gauze or the pottery, both of which are insuperable obstacles. So we need have no fear of escape.

But this is not enough. While we have to see to our own safety, we must also think of the captives' welfare. The dwelling is hygienic and easy to carry into the sun or the shade, as the observation of the moment may demand; but it does not contain the victuals with which the Scorpions, frugal though they be, cannot dispense indefinitely. With a view to feeding them without moving the cover, the trellis-work is pierced at the top with a small opening through which I slip the live game, caught from day to day as needed. After this has been served, a plug of cotton-wool closes the buttery hatch.

My caged specimens, soon after their installation, enable me to watch their work as excavators even better than the occupants of the open-air community, for whom my trowel has prepared an entrance-passage beneath the stones. The Languedocian Scorpion is master of craft; he knows how to house himself in a cell of his own making. In order to establish themselves, each of my interned prisoners has at his disposal a wide, curved potsherd, which, set firmly in the sand, provides the foundation of a grotto, a simple arched fissure. The Scorpion has only to dig beneath this and lodge himself as comfortably as he can.

The excavator does not dally long, especially in the sun, whose glare annoys him. Steadying himself on his fourth pair of legs, the Scorpion rakes the ground with the three other pairs: he turns it over, reducing it to a loose dust with a graceful agility that reminds us of a Dog scratching a hole in which to bury a bone. After the brisk twirling of the legs comes the touch of the broom. With his tail laid flat and relaxed to the utmost, he pushes back the earthy mass, making the same movement as does our elbow when thrusting an obstacle aside. If the rubbish thus shot back be not sufficiently out of the way, the sweeper returns, repeats the process and finishes the job.

Observe that the pincers, notwithstanding their strength, never take part in the digging, even to the extent of extracting a grain of sand. They are reserved for feeding, fighting, and, above all, enquiry, and would lose the exquisite sensitiveness of their fingers if used for that heavy task. In this way the legs and tail, in repeated alternations, scratch the soil and thrust the rubbish outside. At last the worker disappears beneath the potsherd. A mound of sand obstructs the entrance to the vault. At moments we see it shaking and partly slipping, signs that the work is still going on with a further shooting of rubbish, until the cell attains a suitable size. When the hermit wants to go out, he will, without difficulty push back the crumbling barricade.

The Black Scorpion of our houses has not this capacity for making himself a crypt. He is found in the mortar collected at the bottom of walls, the woodwork disjointed by the damp, the rubbish-heaps in dark places, but he restricts himself to using these refuges as he finds them, being unable to improve the hiding-place by his own industry. He does not know how to dig. This ignorance is apparently due to his feeble broom, his smooth, slender tail, very different from the Languedocian's, which is powerful and armed with knotty protuberances.

In the open air, the colony in the enclosure finds a lodging modelled by my care. Under the flat stones where I have contrived to outline a cell in the sandy earth, each of them at once disappears and labours to complete the work, as I perceived by the mound heaped upon the threshold. Wait a few more days and lift the stone: at a depth of three or four inches we see the lair, the burrow, occupied at night and open also by day, when the weather is bad. Sometimes a sudden bend widens the recess into a spacious chamber. In front of the mansion, immediately under the stone, is the entrance-hall.

This, by day, in the hours of blazing sunshine, is where the solitary prefers to be, in the blessed heat gently shaded by the stone. When turned out of this hot bath, his supreme felicity, he brandishes his knotty tail and swiftly retreats indoors, out of reach of the light and of our eyes. Replace the stone and come back fifteen minutes later: we shall find him once more on the threshold of the cavern, where it is so pleasant when a generous sun warms the roof.

The cold season is thus passed in a very monotonous fashion. Both in the hamlet of the enclosure and the menagerie of the cages, the Scorpions go out neither by day nor at night, as I observe by the barricade of sand which remains untouched at the entrance to the home. Are they torpid? Not a bit of it! My frequent visits show them always ready for action, with curved and threatening tails. If the weather grows cooler, they retreat to the bottom of their burrows; if it is fine, they return to the threshold to warm their backs by the touch of the sunny stone. Nothing more for the moment: the anchorite's life is spent in long spells of meditation, either in the cool moist crypt or under the porch of the house, behind the sandy barricade.

In the course of April a sudden change takes place. In the cages, the shelter of the potsherds is abandoned. Gravely the occupants roam around the arena, clamber up the trellis and stand there, even by day. Several of them sleep out and do not go home again, preferring the out-of-door distractions to soft slumbers in the alcove under ground.

In the hamlet in the enclosure, events are more serious. Some of the inhabitants, selected from the smaller, leave the house at night and go wandering without my knowing what becomes of them. I expect to see them return at the end of their stroll, for no other part of the paddock has stones to suit them. Well, not one comes home; all that have gone have disappeared for good. Soon the big ones also display the same vagabond mood; and at last the emigration becomes so active that a moment is at hand when I shall have nothing left of my free colony. Farewell to my lovingly cherished plans! The open-air community, on which I based my fondest hopes, becomes rapidly depopulated; its inhabitants make off, vanish I know not whither. All my seeking fails to recover a single one of the runaways.

Great ill calls for great remedies. I need an insuperable precinct, much more extensive than that of the cages, which establishments do not give scope to the pastimes of my specimens. I have a forcing-frame in which some fleshy plants are stored during the winter. It goes to a depth of three feet into the ground. The brick work is plastered and smoothed with all the care that the mason's trowel and wet rag can give it. I cover the bottom with fine sand and large flat stones distributed here and there. Having made these preparations, I instal inside the frame, each under his own stone, the remaining Scorpions, and those which I have captured this very morning complete my collection. With the aid of this vertical barrier shall I this time retain my specimens and see what interests me so greatly?

I shall see nothing at all. Next morning, all of them, old and new, have disappeared. There were twenty of them: and not one remains. Had I reflected ever so little, I should have expected this. At the season of persistent rain, in the autumn, how often have I not found the Black Scorpion hiding in the crevices of the windows? Fleeing the dampness of his usual retreats, the dark corners of the yards, he has clambered up to me by scaling the front wall to the height of the first storey. The slight roughness of the plaster was enough to enable his grapnels to make the perpendicular ascent.

Despite his corpulence, the Languedocian is as good a climber as the Black Scorpion. I have a proof of it before my eyes. A barrier three feet high, as smooth as a wash of common mortar can make it, has not stopped one of my captives. In a single night, the whole band has decamped from the frame.

Rearing in the open air, even within walls, is recognized as being impracticable: the lack of discipline in the flock nullifies the shepherd's devices. One resource alone remains, that of internment under cover. Thus the year ends, with some ten pans standing on the large table in my study. Out of doors is prohibited: those night prowlers, the cats, seeing something move about in my appliances, would upset everything.

On the other hand, the population is restricted under each cover and amounts to two or three inhabitants at most. There is no space. In the absence of a sufficiency of neighbours and also of the violent exposure to the sun which they enjoyed on their native hills, the prisoners on my table seem smitten with home-sickness and hardly respond to my expectations. Cowering under their potsherds or hanging to the trellis, most of them slumber, dreaming of liberty. The small results which I obtain from my bored specimens is far from satisfying me. I want something more than this. The close of the year is spent in gleaning petty facts and making plans for a better establishment.

The outcome of these plans is a glazed prison whose panes will give no hold to the grapnels and will make climbing impossible. The joiner builds me a frame, the glazier completes the work. I myself varnish the woodwork, so as to make the uprights very slippery. The structure looks like four window-frames placed side by side and put together to form a rectangle. The bottom is a flooring with a layer of sand. A lid covers it altogether when the weather is cold and especially when the rain threatens a flood, which would have disastrous effects on this undrained ground. It is raised more or less high according to the state of the day. The enclosure has ample room for two dozen chambers, each with its potsherd and its occupant. Moreover, wide alleys and spacious cross-roads allow long walks to be taken without hindrance.

Well, at the very moment when I believe myself to have solved the housing-question satisfactorily, I perceive that the glazed park will not retain its population long, if I do not invent a remedy. The glass stops short any attempt at scaling: for lack of adhesive sandals, the Scorpions cannot grip a surface of this kind. They flounder against the panes, it is true, and raise themselves to their full length on the support of their tail: an excellent buttress, but they have hardly left the ground before they fall back again, heavily.

Things go wrong in respect of the wooden uprights, though these are made as narrow as possible and varnished with particular care. The stubborn climbers clamber little by little along these smooth tracks; they halt from time to time, clinging to the greasy pole, and then resume the difficult ascent. I surprise some who have reached the top and are on the point of escaping. My tweezers replace them in the fold. As the ventilation of the home demands that the lid should remain raised during the greater part of the day, the place would soon be wholly deserted if I did not see to it.

I think of greasing the uprights with a mixture of oil and soap. This restrains the fugitives slightly, without succeeding in stopping them. Their delicate little claws manage to sink into the pores of the wood through the substance coating it and the ascent begins anew. Let us try a non-porous obstacle. I hang the walls with glazed paper. This time the difficulty is insurmountable for the big, pot-bellied ones; it is not quite so effective with regard to the others, who, being nimbler in their gait, try to hoist themselves up and often succeed in doing so. I get the better of them only by glossing the glazed paper with soot.

Henceforth there are no more escapes, though attempts at flight continue. Coming after the experiment with the forcing-frames, these feats of prowess on slippery surfaces tell us all there is to learn about an aptitude which the animal's corpulence was far from leading us to suspect. Like his black colleague who enters our houses, the Languedocian Scorpion is a skilled climber.

Behold me then the owner of three establishments, each possessing its advantages and its defects: the free colony at the end of the paddock; the wire-gauze cages in my study; and lastly the glazed rock-garden. I shall consult them turn and turn about, especially the last. To the evidence supplied in this manner we will add the rare data gathered from stones turned over on the original sites. The Scorpions' luxurious Crystal Palace, now the leading curiosity of my home, stands all the year round in the open air, on a bench at a few steps from my door. Not a member of the family passes it without a glance. Taciturn creatures, shall I succeed in making you speak?

1 Thursday is a whole holiday in the French schools. At this time the author was a schoolmaster at Avignon. Cf. *The Life of the Fly*, by J. Henri Fabre, translated by Alexander Teixeira de Mattos: chaps. xix and xx.—*Translator's Note.*

2 *Scolopendra cingulata*, the centipede.—*Translator's Note.*

3 Cf. *The Life of the Spider*, by J. Henri Fabre, translated by Alexander Teixeira de Mattos: *passim.*—*Translator's Note.*

4 More recent opinion conceives the comb or picten as originally the respiratory organ of an aquatic ancestor of *Scorpio*, now probably serving as a guide or clasper when pairing.—*"B. W."*

5 For the Narbonne Lycosa, or Black-bellied Tarantula, cf. *The Life of the Spider*: chaps. i and iii to vi.—*Translator's Note.*

6 The enclosed paddock, or piece of waste land, in which the author used to study his insects in their natural state. Cf. *The Life of the Fly*: chap. i.—*Translator's Note.*

CHAPTER II
THE LANGUEDOCIAN SCORPION: FOOD

I begin by learning that, despite his terrible weapon, a likely token of brigandage and gluttony, the Languedocian Scorpion is an extremely frugal eater. When I visit him at home, among the pebbles of the adjacent hills, I carefully ransack his haunts in the hope of coming upon the remains of an ogre's feast, and I come upon nothing more than the crumbs of a hermit's collation: in fact, as a rule, I find nothing at all. A few green wing-cases belonging to some Tree bug; wings of the adult Ant-lion; dismembered segments of a puny Locust: these make up my list.

The hamlet in the paddock, assiduously consulted, tells me more. After the fashion of a valetudinarian who lives on a diet and eats at stated hours, the Scorpion has his feeding-season. For six or seven months, from October till April, he does not leave his dwelling, though always fit and ready to wield his tail. During this period, if I put any sort of food within his reach, he sweeps it out of the burrow with the back of his tail and pays it no further attention.

It is at the end of March that the first cravings of the stomach are aroused. At this season, on inspecting the cabins, I sometimes find one or other of my specimens quietly gnawing at a capture, a meagre Myriapod, such as a Cryptops or Lithobius. For that matter, the frequency of the item is far from making up for its smallness; and it is long before the consumer of the scanty morsel finds himself in possession of a second.

I expected something better:

"A brute like that," I said to myself, "so well armed for battle, cannot be content with trifles. We do not load our pea-shooters with a charge of dynamite to bring down a Sparrow: that awful sting was never meant to stab a humble little animal. The Scorpion's food must be some powerful quarry."

I was wrong. Terribly equipped for fighting though he be, the Scorpion is an indifferent hunter.

He is a poltroon into the bargain. A little Mantis, come into being that same day and encountered on the road, fills him with dismay. A Cabbage Butterfly1 puts him to flight merely by beating the ground with her clipped wings: the harmless cripple overawes his cowardice. It needs the stimulus of hunger to persuade him to attack.

What am I to give him, when his appetite begins to awaken in April? Like the Spiders, he requires a live prey, seasoned with blood that is not yet congealed: he requires a morsel quivering in the throes of death. He never eats a corpse. The game, moreover, must be tender and of small size. Thinking to give him a treat, in the early days of my experience as a rearer of Scorpions, I offered him Locusts, picking out the biggest. He obstinately refused them. They were too tough, and, besides, too difficult to handle, owing to their kicks, which demoralize the coward.

I try the Field Cricket,2 with a belly as plump and luscious as a pat of butter. I drop half-a-dozen into the glazed enclosure, with a leaf of lettuce which will console them for the horrors of the lions' den. The singers seem not to heed their terrible neighbours; they sing their little songs and nibble at their salad. If a strolling Scorpion appears upon the scene, they look at him: they point their slender antennæ in his direction, without any other sign of perturbation at the approach of the passing monster. He, on his side, draws back as soon as he sees them: he is afraid of getting into trouble with these strangers. Should he touch one of them with the tip of his pincers, forthwith he flees, overcome with terror. The six Crickets spend a month with the wild beasts and none takes note of them. They are too big, too fat. My six patients are restored to freedom as safe and sound as when they entered the cage.

I serve up Woodlice, Glomeres,3 Iuli, all the rabble of the rocks beloved of the Scorpion; I make a trial with Asidæ4 and Opatra which, assiduous lurkers under the stones in the actual places frequented by the hunters, might well be the customary game; I offer Clythra-beetles,5 gathered on the brushwood beside the burrows, and Cicindelæ6 captured on the sand in my guests' very domain: nothing, absolutely nothing is accepted, apparently because of the ungrateful exterior.

Where shall I find that modest mouthful, at once tender and savoury? Chance provides me with it. In May I am visited by a Beetle with soft wing-cases, *Omophlus lepturoides*, a finger's-breadth long. He arrived suddenly in the enclosure in swarms. Around an ilex all yellow with catkins there is a whirling cloud of Beetles, flying, settling, sipping sweets and frantically attending to their love-affairs. This life of revelry lasts a fortnight: then they all disappear in caravans going one knows not whither. On behalf of my boarders, we will levy on these nomads, who look to me as though they would be suitable. I was right in my assumption. After a long, a very long wait, I see the Scorpion make a meal. Here he comes, stealthily advancing towards the insect motionless on the ground. He does not hunt his quarry: he gathers it in. There is neither hurry nor contest, no movement of the tail, no use of the poisoned weapon. The Scorpion placidly grabs the morsel with his two-fingered hands; the pincers bend back, carry it to the mouth and then both hold it until it is all consumed. The insect that is being eaten, full of life, struggles between the mandibles, to the resentment of the eater, who likes to nibble quietly.

Then the dart bends down before the mouth; very gently it pricks the insect once or twice and paralyses it. The mastication is resumed and the sting continues to tap, as though the consumer were swallowing the morsel a forkful at a time.

At last the insect, patiently chewed and chewed again for hours on end, has become a dry pellet which the stomach would refuse; but this residue has entered the gullet so far that the sated Scorpion cannot always reject it directly. The intervention of the pincers is required to extricate it. One of them seizes the pill with the finger-tips, daintily extracts it from the throat and drops it to the ground. The meal is finished: it will not be repeated for a long time to come.

A great improvement on the wire-gauze covers, the large glazed cage, full of animation in the evening twilight, provides me with abundant information touching this strange frugality. In April and May, essentially the season of festive assemblies and banquets, I provision the place lavishly with game. At this time my lilac-walk abounds with Cabbage Butterflies and Swallowtails. Caught in the net, their wings partly amputated, a dozen of these Butterflies are let loose in the establishment, whence their maimed condition will prevent them from escaping.

In the evening, at about eight o'clock, the wild beasts leave their lairs. They stop for a moment on the threshold of their potsherds to enquire into the state of things; then, gathering from more or less all directions, they begin to stroll to and fro, with their tails now uplifted now trailing behind them with the tip always curling upwards. The mood of the moment and the objects encountered determine the posture. The discreet light of a lantern hung outside the panes allows me to watch events.

The mutilated Butterflies whirl in short flights over the ground. Through this desperately fluttering mob the Scorpions pass to and fro, knocking them over and trampling on them, without taking further notice of them. Sometimes, in the hazards of this scrimmage, one of the cripples settles on the ogre's back. He does not mind these familiarities, makes no protest and carries his unaccustomed rider up and down. Some of the heedless creatures fling themselves under the strollers' pincers; others actually touch the horrible mouth. It makes no difference: the Scorpions disdain their food.

A similar experiment is repeated nightly, so long as Pieres abound on the lilac-bushes. My catering leads to very little. From time to time, however, I witness a capture. A Butterfly fluttering on the ground is grabbed by one of the promenaders. The Scorpion quickly snaps her up without a pause and goes his way, with his pincers still groping and held before him like a pair of distraught arms. This time, the hands do not keep the morsel within reach of the mouth, being otherwise occupied in reconnoitring the path followed: it is the mandibles only that carry the booty. The Butterfly, eaten alive, desperately flaps what is left of her wings. She produces the impression of a white plume waving on the crest of the savage victor. If the captive's struggles become excessively inconvenient, the spoiler, still walking along and munching, quiets her with little pats of his sting. At last he flings the prize away. What has he eaten? Just the head, no more.

Less often, others hasten to convey the booty to their lairs beneath the potsherds. Here the meal will be taken far from the madding crowd. Others, after securing their capture, withdraw to a corner of the enclosure and refresh themselves in the open, with their belly on the sand.

A week later, after a certain number of these incidents, I inspect the place and examine the caves one by one, to ascertain the amount of provisions consumed. The wings, those uneatable leavings, will enlighten me in this respect. Well, save for rare exceptions, there are no wings detached from the corpses. Nearly all the Butterflies are intact; they have dried up without being eaten. A few of them, three or four, have been decapitated. The results of my conscientious investigations are limited to this. During a week, in the full swing of activity, a tiny mouthful has been enough for these head-eaters. There are twenty-five of them in my establishment, twenty-five sated with a crumb.

To them the Butterfly must be an almost unknown fare. It is doubtful whether, down in their rocky labyrinths, they ever capture such game, which loves tall blossoms and sinuous flights. Unfamiliar with this quarry, they may disdain it, merely taking a bite in the absence of food more to their taste. Now what can they find in their wild, sun-parched territory?

Locusts apparently. Crickets, a horde that is never lacking wherever there is a blade of grass to nibble. It is on these that I rely by preference when the season of the Pieres and other ordinary Butterflies closes. The paddock then abounds in Crickets and Locusts, a very youthful generation, clad only in a short jacket. These are surely the proper diet for my Scorpions, with their love of tender mouthfuls. Some are green, others grey; some fat, others thin; some are mounted on stilts, others are squat and short-shanked. The consumers can make their choice amid this varied assortment.

At nightfall, in the area faintly lighted by the lantern, I distribute my crop of Locusts, who are fairly quiet at this late hour. The Scorpions lose no time in making their appearance. The living manna is wriggling all about them. At the least tap, the nearest strollers decamp; they find things too exciting. It is an exact repetition of the experiments with the Butterflies: none sets any store by the tit-bits, most certainly seen and even touched, for the Scorpions often encounter them and walk on them.

I see a Locust who, as luck will have it, has got caught in the fingers of a passing Scorpion; and the latter is too good-natured even to close his pincers. Ever so gentle a squeeze would put him in possession of an excellent head of game; and heedlessly he allows it to slip away. I see a little Green Locust hoisted by accident on the back of a promenader, a terrible mount that carries her quietly, without dreaming of harming her. A hundred times I witness face-to-face meetings, defensive retreats, swishes of the tail that sweep aside the heedless creature encountered on the highway, but never any serious hand-to-hand fighting, still less pursuit. It is only at rare intervals that my daily observations show me one or other of my frugal eaters in possession of a Locust.

At pairing-time, in April and May, a sudden change of behaviour turns the sober Scorpion into a glutton and makes her indulge in scandalous orgies. At this season I often come upon a Scorpion in the enclosure, under her tile, devouring one of her own kind in perfect quietude, as she might devour an ordinary head of game. Everything goes down, except, as a rule, the tail, which remains hanging for whole days from the sated creature's jaws and is finally rejected as though with regret. It may be presumed that the poison-phial at the end of the joint has something to do with this refusal. Perhaps the toxic fluid has a flavour which is unpleasant to the consumer's taste.

Apart from this remnant, the devoured Scorpion disappears entirely into a belly whose capacity seems inferior in bulk to the things swallowed. It takes a very obliging stomach to find room for such a dish. Before being chewed and packed away, the contents must be larger than the container. Now these Gargantuan banquets are not normal reflections but matrimonial rites, to which we shall have occasion to return. They take place only in the mating-season: and the animals devoured are always males.

I shall not therefore enter these Scorpions who die victims of their embraces on the list of normal victuals. What we see here is the aberrations of an animal at rutting-time, wedding-orgies worthy of figuring beside the tragic nuptials of the Praying Mantis.7 Nor shall I enter the feasts provoked by my artifices, when I confront the Scorpion with a powerful adversary and worry the two combatants in my eagerness to see the duel. Thus exasperated, the Scorpion defends himself and stabs; then, in the intoxication of his victory, he eats the fallen foe, in so far as his swallowing-faculties permit. This is his manner of celebrating his triumph. Never, but for my intervention, would he have dared to attack such an enemy; never would he have bitten into such a bulky prey.

Apart from these banquets, which are too exceptional to be taken into account, I note none but frugal collations. My vigilance is perhaps at fault; it might well be that the consumption is greater at late hours of the night, in the absence of witnesses; and therefore, before granting the Scorpion a certificate for extreme moderation in diet, I appeal to the following experiment, which will give us a definite reply.

Early in autumn, four medium-sized specimens are installed separately, each in a saucer furnished with a layer of fine sand and a potsherd. A pane of glass closes the receptacle, prevents the escape of the skilful climbers and allows the sun to enliven the dwelling. Without keeping out the air, the lid is enough to prevent any small game, such as Clothes-moths or Mosquitoes, from entering the enclosed space. The four saucers are deposited in a conservatory where a tropical temperature holds sway for the greater part of the day. No provisions are served by me, nor will the least mouthful ever arrive from the outside, unless it be some vagrom Ant. In this total absence of provisions, what will become of the interned Scorpions?

Always brisk and lively without a scrap of food, they go to earth under the potsherd. They rummage about and dig themselves a burrow closed by a barrier of sand. From time to time, especially in the evening twilight, they issue from their lair, take a short stroll and then go home again, behaving just as though they had been fed.

When the cold sets in, though it is not freezing in the green-house, the prisoners no longer leave their home, which has been dug a little deeper in anticipation of the severe weather. Their health, for that matter, continues excellent. When I inspect them, as my curiosity often prompts me to do, I find them always fit and ready to repair the burrow which I have disturbed.

Winter ends without mishap. There is nothing unusual in this: the cold season, while suspending activity, moderates or even does away with the need for refection. But the heat returns and, with it, the need of food, which calls for provisions. Now what do the fasters do while their kinsmen in the glass cage are restoring their strength with Butterflies and Locusts? Are they languid and anæmic? Not at all.

Quite as vigorous as those who have been feeding, they brandish their gnarled tails and reply to my teasing with threatening gestures. If I worry them too much, they run away quickly along the circumference of the saucer. Famine does not seem to have tried them. This cannot go on indefinitely. About the middle of June, three of the captives die; the fourth holds out till July. It has taken nine months of absolute abstinence to put an end to their activity.

Another test is arranged for very young specimens, about a couple of months old. They measure about an inch in length, from the forehead to the tip of the tail. Their colouring is brighter than that of the adults; the pincers in particular look as though they were carved out of amber and coral. The future horror has his attractive points in early youth.—I find them under the stones from October onwards. Invariably solitary like their elders, they dig themselves, under the chosen shelter, a little hole barricaded by a sandy mound consisting of the rubbish of the excavations. When taken from their retreat, they run along nimbly, curving their tails over their backs and brandishing their fragile stings.

In October I place four of them in as many tumblers closed with a muslin veil, an insuperable obstacle to any tiny prey coming from the outside. The prisoners have for digging purposes a finger's-breadth of fine sand and as shelter a small disk of cardboard. Well, these little fellows undergo abstinence as pluckily as the adults and are still active and restless in the months of May and June.

These two experiments prove to us that the Scorpion, while retaining his activity, is capable of dispensing with food during three fourths of the year. It must therefore take a long time to make him corpulent.

A caterpillar that lives only a few days is continually browsing to accumulate the substance of the future Butterfly; its voracious appetite makes up for the shortness of the banquet. How does the Scorpion contrive to hoard so much matter out of crumbs so few and far between? With him the accumulation of tissue must be the work of exceptional longevity.

It is not very difficult to arrive at an approximate estimate of his length of life. The stones turned over at different periods give us the answer as clearly as the archives of a record-office would do. I find, in respect of size, five classes of Scorpions. The smallest measure two-thirds of an inch in length; the largest four inches. Between these two extremes, three sizes are quite distinctly discernible.

Beyond a doubt, each of these categories corresponds with a year's difference in age, perhaps even more, for each stage seems to be a protracted one; at all events the progress in size is hardly perceptible, at the end of a year, in the specimens in my rearing-cages. The Languedocian Scorpion therefore boasts the prerogative of a green old age: he lives five years and probably longer. He has ample time, as we see, to wax fat on scraps.

To grow big is not everything: activity is essential. The scraps will be repeated, it is true, but always so sparingly and at such distant intervals that we begin to wonder what part eating really plays in this instance. My prisoners, large and small, subjected to a strict fast, give especial cause for reflection. Whenever I disturb their repose—and my curiosity deprives itself of few opportunities—they move about briskly, brandishing their tails, delving the sand, sweeping it, shifting it; in short, they expend many kilogram-metres of energy, to use the technical expression; and this goes on for eight or nine months.

In performing this work what do they expend on materials? Nothing. From the first day of their imprisonment all food is cut off. The thought occurs to the mind of nutritive reserves, of adipose savings accumulated in the organism. The animal, according to this, in order to balance the expenditure of energy, would live upon itself.

With portly adults the explanation would be valid in a certain measure; but I have subjected lean specimens, of medium age, to the test; I have selected young ones, just beginning life. What can these small Scorpions have in their bellies? What do they possess that can be transformed into motor energy by vital oxidation? The scalpel cannot find it and the imagination refuses to appraise it, so great is the disproportion between the amount of work accomplished and the worker's bulk. If the whole animal were before all a combustible and were to burn to the last atom, the total sum of heat emitted would still be far from equivalent to the total sum of the mechanical effects. Our factories cannot keep an engine going, all the year round, with a lump of coal as its whole provision.

My Scorpions hardly seem to consume even this lump of fuel. After a long and rigorous abstinence, they are as fresh and brightly-coloured, as glossy with health as at the beginning of the experiment.

We can understand the Snail, sunk in a deep inertia and contracted within his shell, whose opening he has closed with a chalky lid or a parchment cover: he no longer eats, but neither does he see; he exists on his reserves by slowing down his vital processes to the lowest possible limits. The Scorpion, always moving about, despite the excessive prolongation of the fast, is beyond our comprehension.

For the third time in the course of our studies, with reference to the young first of the Lycosa8, then of the Clotho Spider9, and now of the Scorpion, we are led back to the same suspicion. Is it a fact that animals of an organization very different from our own, deprived of an individual temperature determined by an active oxidation, are governed by biological laws which are immutable in the whole series of living creatures? Need movement in them be always the result of combustion for which eating would furnish the materials? Might they not derive their activity, at least in part, from the circumambient energies, heat, electricity, light and so on, varying modes of the same motive power?

These energies are the soul of the world, the unfathomable vortex which sets the material universe in motion. Would it then be paradoxical to picture the animal in certain cases as a highly perfected accumulator, capable of collecting the circumambient heat, of transmuting it in its tissues into a mechanical equivalent and of returning it in the form of motion? This would suggest a possibility that the animal might perform work in the absence of energizing matter absorbed as food.

Ah, life made a superb discovery when, in prehistoric times, it invented the Scorpion! To work without eating: what an incomparable gift, had it become general! What miseries, what horrors would be abolished, if we were freed from the tyranny of the stomach! Why was this wonderful attempt not continued, why was it not perfected in creatures of a higher order? What a pity that the initial example was not followed in an ever-increasing progression! Then perhaps to-day, exempted from the ignominious hunt for food, thought, the loftiest and most delicate expression of activity, would restore itself after fatigue with a ray of sunshine.

Of this gift of yore, full of unrealized promises, certain constituents have nevertheless been disseminated throughout the animal kingdom. We ourselves live by solar radiation; we derive part of our energy from it. The Arab, supporting existence on a handful of dates, is no less active than the man of the north, gorged with meat and beer; though he does not fill his stomach so plentifully, he has a bigger share in the banquet of the sun.

All things considered then, the Scorpion must derive the main part of his energizing food from the circumambient warmth. As for the plastic food indispensable to physical growth, its turn comes, a little sooner or later, announced by a moult. The stiff tunic splits along the back; the animal slips gently out of its cast clothes, which have become too tight. Then comes the imperious call for food, were it only to make good the cost of the new skin. Henceforth, if the fast continues, my prisoners, especially the smaller ones, die before long.

1 Or Large White Butterfly. Cf. *The Life of the Caterpillar*, by J. Henri Fabre, translated by Alexander Teixeira de Mattos: chap. xiv.—*Translator's Note.*

2 Cf. *The Life of the Grasshopper*: chaps. xv and xvi.—*Translator's Note.*

3 Pill-Millipedes.—*Translator's Note.*

4 Worm-like Millipedes.—*Translator's Note.*

5 Cf. *The Glow-worm and Other Beetles*, by J. Henri Fabre, translated by Alexander Teixeira de Mattos. Chaps. xv and xvi.—*Translator's Note.*

6 *Tiger-Beetles.*—*Translator's Note.*

7 Cf. *The Life of the Grasshopper*: chaps. vi to ix and in particular chap. vii.—*Translator's Note.*

8 Cf. *The Life of the Spider*: chap vi.—*Translator's Note.*

9 Cf. *idem*: chap. xvi.—*Translator's Note.*

CHAPTER III
THE LANGUEDOCIAN SCORPION: THE POISON

In attacking small game, his usual fare, the Scorpion hardly uses his weapon. He seizes the insect with his two pincers and thus holds it the whole time within reach of his mouth, which nibbles slowly. Sometimes, if the victim struggles and disturbs the repast, the tail comes curving down and, with a series of little taps, deprives the patient of the power of movement. When all is said, the sting plays but a very subordinate part in the acquisition of food.

It is really of no use to the animal except in a moment of danger, face to face with an enemy. I do not know against what foes the formidable beast may have to defend itself. Who among the frequenters of the stony wastes would venture to attack it? Though I do not know on what occasions, in the normal course of things, the Scorpion is obliged to take measures of defence. I can at least resort to artifice and arrange encounters which will force him to fight in grim earnest. To judge of the violence of his poison, I propose to place him in the presence of various powerful foes, without leaving the domain of entomology.

A Languedocian Scorpion and a Narbonne Lycosa are put into a large jar, with a layer of sand at the bottom, which affords a less slippery foothold than the glass. The two are similarly equipped with poisonous fangs. Which of the two will gain the upper hand and eat the other? While the Lycosa is the less powerful, she has the advantage of agility, which enables her to leap on her adversary and attack him unexpectedly. Before the defender, who is slow in countering, is able to adopt the fighting attitude, the other will deliver her stroke and flee before the brandished sting. The chances would seem to favour the active Spider.

The events do not correspond with these probabilities. So soon as she perceives the enemy, the Lycosa stands half-erect, opens her fangs, on which a drop of poison is gathering, and boldly waits. The Scorpion approaches with short steps, extending his pincers in front of him. With his two-fingered hands he seizes and holds the Spider, who protests desperately, opening and closing her fangs without being able to bite, kept as she is at a distance. The struggle becomes impossible with such an adversary, armed with long pincers which hold the foe helpless at arm's length and prevent her approach.

Without any sort of contest, therefore, the Scorpion curves his tail, brings it down in front of his forehead and drives the sting, entirely at his ease, into the victim's black breast. This is not the instantaneous thrust of the Wasps and the other four-winged fighters: to make the weapon penetrate requires a certain effort. The knotted tail pushes, swaying slightly: it turns the sting to and fro as we twist a pointed tool with our fingers to make it enter a hard substance. When the hole is made, the sting lingers in the wound for a moment, doubtless to allow time for a larger dose of virus to escape. The result is overwhelming. No sooner is the sturdy Lycosa stung than she draws up her legs. She is dead.

I have treated myself to this stirring spectacle with half-a-dozen victims. What the first experiment showed me the others repeated. There is always the instant attack by the Scorpion the moment he sees the Lycosa, always the tactics of the tongs holding the enemy at a distance, always the sudden death of the spitted Spider. If I crushed the animal underfoot, the inertia produced would be no more immediate. It is as though the Lycosa had been struck dead by lightning.

To eat the vanquished enemy is the rule, all the more inasmuch as the plump Spider is a magnificent prey, such as but rarely falls to the Scorpion's lot in his usual hunting-grounds. Then and there, without delay, he sits down to his meal, commencing with the head, his customary routine with any sort of game. Motionless, he crunches and swallows, in tiny mouthfuls. Everything is consumed, excepting a few joints of the legs, which are tough morsels. The Gargantuan feast lasts for twenty-four hours.

When the banquet is over, we wonder how the dish has managed to disappear into a belly hardly larger than the thing eaten. Those who are exposed to interminable fasts, and are compelled to gorge themselves to excess when the occasion offers, must have special digestive powers.

If the Scorpion attacks the Lycosa, who would be capable of making a serious defence were she to rush upon the enemy, instead of proudly standing with her breast uncovered, what will be the fate of the meek Epeiræ?1 All, even the largest, the Angular, the Banded, and the Silky Epeira, are fiercely attacked, all the more since these poor spinners, demoralized by fear, do not even try to fling their hanks of cord, which so promptly paralyse the assailant. In their webs, with a lavish discharge of snares, they would master the ferocious Mantis,2 the formidable Hornet, or the big Locust, that expert kicker. Away from their own homes, faced by an enemy and not a victim, they utterly forget their potent methods of binding the foe.

When stung, they all instantly succumb, struck dead like the Lycosa; and the Scorpion feasts upon them.

Under the stone, the Spider-lover never meets the Lycosa or the Epeiræ, who frequent other regions; but he may, at long intervals, find other Spiders, addicted like himself to sheltering in rocky refuges, and notably the timid Clotho.[3] He is therefore pretty familiar with this sort of game, and any fair-sized Spider suits him, provided that he be hungry.

I suspect him of being by no means indifferent to the capture of a Praying Mantis, another highly meritorious dish. Certainly he does not go in search of her on the bushes, the usual resort of this ravenous insect: his means of climbing, which are excellently adapted to scaling a wall, would never permit him to walk on the wavering support of the leaves. He must strike when the mother is pregnant, towards the end of the summer. As a matter of fact, I fairly often find the nest of the Praying Mantis fastened to the lower surface of the lumps of stone haunted by the Scorpion.

The highwayman may make his approach, in quest of victuals, on a peaceful night, just when the labouring mother is whipping the froth of her egg-filled casket.[4] What happens then I have never witnessed; probably I never shall: it would be asking too much of luck. Let us fill the gap by artificial means.

In the cock-pit of an earthenware dish, I provoke a duel between a Scorpion and a Mantis, both selected of a good size. If necessary, I stimulate them, urge them to the encounter. I already know that not all the blows of the tail take effect: very often they are mere raps on the head. Sparing of his poison and scorning to sting when there is no pressing need, the Scorpion repels the intruder with a sudden back stroke of the tail, without using the needle. In our various experiments we will count only the blows which draw blood in proof that the sting has penetrated.

When seized with the tweezers, the Mantis instantly adopts the spectral attitude,[5] with the saw-toothed legs open and the wings displayed like an heraldic crest. This scare-crow attitude, so far from succeeding, makes the attack all the easier: the sting plunges into the base, between the two lethal limbs, and lingers for some time in the wound. When it is withdrawn, there is still a drop of poison oozing at the tip.

Then and there the Mantis draws up her legs in the throes of death. The belly heaves, the caudal appendages wave by fits and starts, the tarsi give faint quivers. On the other hand, the lethal legs, the antennæ, and the mouth-parts are motionless. This condition is followed, in less than fifteen minutes, by complete inertia.

The Scorpion does not think out his blows; he strikes at random any point within reach. This time he has stabbed a part which is eminently vulnerable, because of the proximity of the principal nerve-centres; he has stung the Mantis in the breast, between the lethal legs, precisely where the Mantis-killing Tachytes6 wounds her victim with the object of paralysing it. The act is fortuitous and not intentional: the lout is not an expert anatomist like the Wasp. As luck would have it, death was instantaneous. What would happen if the sting were delivered in another, less dangerous part of the body?

I change the operator, to make sure that the poison-phial is charged. I shall take the same precaution in the various subsequent encounters: each fresh victim will have a fresh executioner, whose full powers have been restored by a long rest.

The Mantis, another powerful matron, stands half-erect, turns her head7 and looks at him warily over her shoulder. She assumes her spectral attitude, with puffing sounds produced by rubbing the wings together. Her boldness at first succeeds: she manages to seize her adversary's tail with her toothed fore-arms. As long as she holds tight, the Scorpion is disarmed and unable to hurt her.

But fatigue supervenes, enhanced by terror. The Mantis had seized the tail brandished in front of her as she might have harpooned any other part of the body, without doubting the efficiency of her manœuvre. The poor simpleton opens her trap. She is lost. The Scorpion stings her in the abdomen, not far from the third pair of legs. Complete collapse ensues, like that of a piece of clockwork whose mainspring is broken.

It is not in my power to obtain stings at this or that point as I choose: the irascible Scorpion does not lend himself to the liberty of attempting to guide his weapon. I make the most of the various instances that occur in the hazards of the contest. Some of them are worth recording, because of the great distance from the centres of innervation.

This time the Mantis is stung on one of the lethal limbs, in the fine-skinned joint of the arm and fore-arm. This results in immediate inertia of the limb affected and soon after of the second. The other legs curl up: there are pulsations of the abdomen; and absolute immobility quickly follows. Death is almost instantaneous.

Another is stung in the joint between the shank and the thigh of one of the middle legs. Suddenly the four hind-legs fold back; the wings which the insect had not outspread at the moment of the attack, are unfurled convulsively, as in the spectral attitude, and remain outspread even after death. The murderous legs flounder about in disorder: they clutch, they open, they close again; the antennæ move, the palpi tremble, the abdomen throbs, the caudal appendages wave to and fro. Another fifteen minutes of this tumultuous death-struggle: and all is still; the Mantis is no more.

And so in all the instances in which my curiosity, greatly excited by the stirring aspect of the tragedy, indulges whatever the point attacked, whether near the nerve-centres or farther away, the Mantis always succumbs, sometimes instantly, sometimes after a few minutes' convulsions. Rattlesnakes, Vipers, Puff-adders and other venomous Snakes of dreadful renown do not kill their victims more promptly.

At first I regarded this as due to a highly-strung organism, which is all the more sensitive and vulnerable because it is better equipped. Picked creatures both, said I to myself, the Spider and the Mantis die instantaneously from an injury which a ruder creature would endure for hours and days, perhaps even without any great inconvenience. Let us then try the Mole-cricket, the detested *Taiocebo* of the Provençal gardener. A strange beast indeed is this root-cutter; powerful, too, clumsy and of a lower type. When you grip it firmly in your hand, it makes you let go by digging into your skin with the toothed toes of its hind-legs, copied from the Mole's.

When brought into contact in a narrow arena, Scorpion and Mole-cricket look each other in the face and seem to recognize each other. Can there have been encounters between them from time to time? It is very doubtful. The Mole-cricket is an inmate of our gardens, of rich soil in which green vegetables convoke underground vermin; the Scorpion is faithful to the sun-scorched slopes on which dry grasses find it difficult to grow. Meetings are hardly probable between the inhabitants of barren and of fruitful soil.

Though unknown to each other, they none the less realize the gravity of the danger confronting them. With no provocation from me, the Scorpion rushes at the Mole-cricket, who, for her part, assumes an aggressive posture, with her shears ready to disembowel her foe. Rubbing her upper wings together, she entones a sort of war-song, a dull buzzing. The Scorpion does not leave her time to finish her ditty; he brings his tail into play. The Mole-cricket's thorax bears a stout, arched cuirass encasing the back. To the rear of this impenetrable armour there is a deep crease, covered with fine skin. It is here that the sting enters. Forthwith, without more ado, the monster is overthrown; she collapses, as though struck by lightning.

Disorderly movements follow. The digging-legs are paralysed; they no longer grip at the straw which I hold out to them. The others thresh to and fro, stretch out and flex themselves again; the four palpi with the large, fleshy tufts meet in a bunch, separate, come together again and pat the object which I place within their reach; the antennæ wave feebly; the belly throbs with deep pulsations. Gradually, these death-throes decrease in violence. At length, in a couple of hours' time, the tarsi, the last to die, cease quivering. The clumsy creature has succumbed no less completely than the Lycosa and the Mantis, but after a longer death-struggle.

It remains to be ascertained whether the stab under the armour of the thorax does not possess a special efficiency, because of the proximity of the nerve-centres. I repeat the experiment with other patients and other operators. Sometimes the sting enters the chink in the armour; more often it touches some part of the abdomen. In this case, even though the stab is delivered at the extreme tip, the result is always sudden death. The only perceptible difference is that, instead of being instantly paralyzed, the digging-legs continue for some time to struggle like the rest. When struck by the Scorpion in any part whatever, the Mole-cricket therefore is always mortally wounded; the powerful insect gives up the ghost after a few convulsive struggles.

Now comes the turn of the Grey Locust,8 the largest and most active of our Acridians. The Scorpion appears perturbed by the proximity of this turbulent kicker. The Locust, on her side, would be only too well pleased to get away. She hops and bumps against the pane of glass with which I have covered the arena to prevent escape. From time to time she drops on the back of the Scorpion, who flees to avoid this sudden fall. At last, losing patience, the runaway stings the Locust in the belly.

The shock must be of extraordinary violence, for one of the big-haunched legs immediately falls off, through one of those spontaneous disarticulations to which Locusts and Grasshoppers are addicted at desperate moments. The other is paralyzed. Stretched straight out and up, it is no longer able to obtain a purchase on the ground. The Locust's hopping-days are over. Meanwhile, the four front legs make disorderly movements and are incapable of progression. When laid on its side, the insect nevertheless turns over and resumes the normal position, all but the large hind-leg, which is still impotent and sticking into the air.

Fifteen minutes pass; and the insect falls, never to rise again. The spasms, the stretching of the legs, the quivering of the tarsi, the waving of the antennæ continue for a long time yet. This condition, becoming more and more aggravated, may last till next day; but sometimes the inertia is complete in less than an hour.

Another powerful Acridian, the Tryxalis9, with the immensely long shanks and the sugar-loaf head, ends like the Locust: her death-agony lasts some hours. Among the sword-bearers, the Grasshoppers, I have seen this gradual paralysis, which is not yet death, but which is no longer life, prolonged for a week. This time the subject is the Vine Ephippiger.10

The pot-bellied creature has been stung in the abdomen. There are cries of distress from the cymbals at the moment of the wound; and the insect falls on its side, with all the appearances of imminent death. Nevertheless the wounded Ephippiger makes a fight for it. At the end of two days, she is kicking so hard with her ataxic legs, incapable of locomotion, that the idea occurs to me to come to her assistance and doctor her up a little. I administer as a cordial, on the tip of a straw, some grape-juice, which is readily accepted.

It seems as though the draught is effectual; the insect appears to be recovering. Nothing of the sort, alas! On the seventh day after the sting, the patient dies. The Scorpion's sting is inexorable, for any insect, even of the strongest. One dies on the spot; another lingers for days; but all succumb in the end. Even though my Ephippiger were to survive for a week, I should know better than to ascribe this to my doctoring with grape-juice: the Grasshopper's long resistance must be attributed to her temperament.

We must consider above all things the gravity of the wound, which varies greatly according to the dose of poison injected. It is not in my power to regulate its emission: besides, the Scorpion is freakish in the flow of the poison from his phial: in one case he is stingy, and in another prodigal. For this reason the discrepancy is great between the data furnished by the Ephippiger. My notes speak of subjects succumbing after a brief interval, whereas others, more numerous, take a long time to die.

Generally, the Grasshoppers resist better than the Locusts. The Ephippiger bears witness to this and, next to her, so does the White-faced Decticus,11 the chief of the sword-bearing clan. The insect with the large mandibles and the ivory head is stabbed near the middle of the abdomen, on the dorsal surface. The wounded Decticus, apparently not gravely injured, walks about and tries to hop. Half an hour later, however, the poison is working. The abdomen is convulsed, curves into a wide hook and, with its open gap, incapable of closing, plows through the rough surface of the soil. The proud creature has become a pitiful cripple. Six hours later, the insect is lying on its side. It exhausts itself in unsuccessful attempts to rise on its feet. Little by little, the crisis subsides. On the second day, the Decticus is dead, really dead: not a limb stirs.

Late in the afternoon, the great black-and-yellow Dragon-fly flies to and fro in a straight line, swiftly and silently, along the hedges. She is the corsair who levies tribute on all who navigate those peaceful waters. Her ardent life, her fiery activity point to a more delicate nervous system than that of the Locust, the placid ruminant of the pastures. And in fact, when stung by the Scorpion, she dies almost as quickly as the Praying Mantis.

The Cicada,12 another spendthrift of energy, who from morning till night, in the dog-days, never ceases singing by jerking his abdomen up and down, beating time to the cadence of his cymbals, likewise dies very speedily. Talents have to be paid for: where the dull-witted hold out, the gifted succumb.

The large Beetles, in their horny armour, are invulnerable. Never will the Scorpion, a clumsy fencer who lunges at random, find the narrow joints in their breast-plates. As for piercing the hard wrapper at some spot or another, this would need a protracted effort, which the patient would hardly permit in the scuffle of his defence. Besides, these boring-tactics are unknown to the brutal Scorpion, who delivers a sudden stab.

One region alone lends itself to the sudden onslaught of the sting. This is the upper surface of the abdomen, which is quite soft and protected by the wing-cases. I uncover this region by holding up the wings and wing-cases with a pair of tweezers; or again I first remove both with the scissors. This mutilation is not a serious matter and would not prevent the patient from surviving quite a long time. The insect is presented to the Scorpion in this condition. It is chosen among the largest, Oryctes,13 Capricorn,14 Scarab,15 Carabus,16 Cetonia,17 Cockchafer,18 Geotrupes.19

All perish by the sting, but the length of the death-struggle varies very greatly. To give a few examples: after convulsive stretching of the limbs, the Scarab Beetle hoists himself on his legs as high as he can, hunches his back and marks time, for lack of co-ordination in the locomotor mechanism. He capsizes, incapable of recovering his footing; he kicks wildly. At length, in a few hours, immobility sets in; the insect is dead.

The Capricorns, *Cerambyx heros*, who lives in the oak, and *C. cerdo*, who lives in the hawthorn and the cherry-laurel, begin in the same way with a sort of cataleptic fit which sometimes lasts for a fairly long time. To some of them death does not come until the next day; others are unable to hold out for more than three or four hours.

The result is the same with the Cetonia or Rose-chafer, the Common Cockchafer, and the magnificently antlered Pine-chafer.20

A pitiful sight is that of the Golden Carabus, or Gold Beetle,21 dying of the sting. Unable to stand on its legs convulsively extended into stilts, the insect tumbles over, picks itself up again, again falls down and again hoists itself to its feet, only to fall once more. The tip of the intestine, with its horny armour, sticks out and swells as though the creature were about to discharge its entrails; the crop belches a black torrent that swamps the head; the golden wing-cases, lifting their cuirass, reveal the poor nudities of the abdomen. Next morning, the tarsi are still quivering. Death is not far off. The swarthy Procrustes, the Gold Beetles's near kinsman, comes to his end in the same wretched fashion. To him we shall return.

Would you, on the other hand, see a stoic, who knows how to die decently? Make the Scorpion sting *Oryctes nasicornis*, commonly known as the Rhinoceros. None of our beetles equals him for hardy bearing. Despite the horn on his nose, he is a peace-lover, dwelling, during his larval period, in old olive-stumps. When stabbed by the Scorpion, he seems at first to feel nothing. He walks about soberly, as usual, and keeps his balance.

But suddenly the atrocious poison works. The legs no longer obey with their customary accuracy; the wounded Beetle staggers and falls on his back. He will never rise again. Lying in this posture for three or four days, with no struggle beyond some vague dying movements, he very quietly gives up the ghost.

How do the Moths and Butterflies behave in their turn? These delicate creatures must be very sensitive to the sting; I am persuaded of it before I put them to the test. Nevertheless, as scrupulous observers, let us experiment. A Swallowtail and a Vulcan perish the moment they are stung. I expected it. The Spurge Hawk-moth and the Striped Hawk-moth offer no more resistance: they too suffer sudden death, just like the Dragon-fly, the Lycosa and the Mantis.

But, to my great surprise, the Great Peacock Moth seems invulnerable. True, the attack is difficult to deliver. The sting goes astray in the soft down, which at each stroke flies away in flocks. Despite repeated blows, I am not sure whether the sting has actually struck home. I accordingly strip the abdomen laying bare the skin. After taking this precaution, I plainly see the weapon driven in. Penetration is now indubitable; it was preceded by other, more doubtful stabs; and yet the big Moth remains impassive.

I place her under a wire-gauze cover standing on the table. She grips the trellis-work and remains there all day long without moving. The wings, outspread to their full width, give not a quiver. Next morning there is no change: the victim of the operation is still hanging to the wires by the hooks of her front tarsi. I remove her and lay her on the table, with her belly uppermost. The big body shakes with rapid tremors. Is this the end?

Not at all. The apparently dying Moth revives, flaps her wings and with a sudden effort, recovers her feet. She climbs up the trellis and again hangs from it. In the afternoon, I lay her on her back for the second time. The wings are actuated by a gentle movement, almost a shudder, as a result of which the prostrate insect glides over the table. It climbs up the trellis again and all movement ceases.

Let us leave the poor Moth in peace: when she is really no more, she will drop off. Well, the fall does not take place until the fourth day after the sting or stings. Life is exhausted. The deceased is a female. The force of maternity, stronger than any mortal terror, postpones death's hour: the Moth laid her eggs before she died.

Should we entertain the very natural thought of attributing this long resistance to the colossus' powerful constitution, the frail product of our Silkworm nurseries, the Mulberry Bombyx, would tell us that we must seek the cause elsewhere. He, the infirm dwarf who has just the strength to beat his wings and flutter round his female, offers no less resistance to the sting than the Great Peacock. The reason for this passivity is probably as follows:

The Great Peacock and the Mulberry-moth are incomplete entities, very different from the Hawk-moth, that ardent explorer of corollas in the gloaming, and the Swallowtail Butterfly and the Mulberry-moth, those untiring pilgrims to the chapel of flowers. They have no mouth implements; they take no nourishment. Deprived of the stimulus of food, they live but a few days, long enough to lay fertile eggs. This diminished vitality must go with a no less delicate and consequently less fragile organism.

Let us descend a few steps in the series of the segmented animals and question the uncouth Millipede. The Scorpion knows him. The colony in the enclosure has shown me the Scorpion feeding on the Cryptops and the Lithobius, the result of his hunting. These to him are harmless mouthfuls, incapable of defence. I propose to-day to place him in touch with the Great Centipede known as the Scolopendra (Smorsitans), the mightiest of our Myriapods.

The dragon with the twenty-two pairs of legs is no stranger to him. I have sometimes found the two together under the same stone. The Scorpion was at home; the other roaming about at night, had taken temporary shelter there. No regrettable incident had ensued from their cohabitation. Is this always so? We shall see.

I confront the two horrors with each other in a large glass jar containing sand. The Centipede goes round and round, hugging the wall of the arena. He is an undulating ribbon, a finger's breadth wide, four or five inches long and ringed with greenish rings on an amber-coloured ground. The long, vibrating antennæ sound the space before him; their tips, sensitive as a finger, encounter the motionless Scorpion. The startled animal instantly turns tail. His circuit brings him back to the foe. There is a fresh contact, followed by a fresh flight.

But the Scorpion is now on his guard, with his arched tail advanced and his pincers open. When the Centipede returns to the dangerous point of his circular track, he is seized with the claws, in the neighbourhood of the head. In vain does the long, flexible animal twine and twist; imperturbably, the Scorpion grips it more firmly than ever with his pincers; and no jerks, windings or unwindings succeed in making him let go.

Meanwhile the sting is at work. Three and four times over it is driven into the sides of the Myriapod, who, for his part, opens wide his poison-fangs and strives to bite, without succeeding in doing so, for the front part of his body is held in the stubborn pincers. The hinder part alone struggles and wriggles, coils and uncoils. These efforts are useless. Kept at a distance by the long tongs, the Scolopendra's poisoned fangs are unable to act. I have seen many insect battles; I know none more horrible than that between these two monstrosities. It is enough to make your flesh creep.

A lull enables me to part the combatants and isolate them. The Centipede licks his bleeding wounds and recovers his strength in a few hours. As for the Scorpion, he has suffered no damage. Next day, a fresh assault is delivered. Three times in succession the Myriapod is stabbed, till the blood flows. Then, fearing reprisals, the Scorpion withdraws, as though frightened by his victory. The wounded animal does not strike back and continues its circular flight. This is enough for to-day. I surround the jar with a cardboard cylinder. When darkness is thus produced, they will both keep quiet.

What happens afterwards, especially at night, I do not know. Probably the battle begins all over again and further thrusts of the sting are delivered. At any rate the Centipede is much weaker on the third day. On the fourth, he is dying. The Scorpion watches him without yet daring to devour him. At last, when there is no more movement, the huge quarry is cut up; the head and then the first two segments are eaten. The dish is too copious; the remainder will go bad and be wasted. His exclusive taste for fresh meat will prevent the Scorpion from touching it.

Though stung seven times and oftener, the Centipede does not die until the fourth day; stung once only, the powerful Lycosa perishes that very instant. Death comes almost as quickly to the Praying Mantis, the Sacred Beetle, the Mole-cricket and other hardy specimens which, if impaled by the collector, would kick and struggle for weeks on the cork slab. Any insect stabbed by the sting finds itself forthwith in a parlous plight; the longest-lived are dead within twenty-four hours; and here we have the Centipedes, pinked seven times over, holding out for four days and perhaps dying from loss of blood as much as from the effects of the poison.

Why these points of difference? Apparently they are a matter of organisation. Life is an equilibrium whose stability varies according to the position in the hierarchy. At the top of the ladder, a fall is easy; at the bottom, there is a firm foothold. The finely-organised insect succumbs, whereas the coarser Millipede resists. Is this really the explanation? The Mole-cricket leaves us undecided. He, the boor, perishes just as quickly as do those refined creatures, the Butterfly and the Mantis. No, we do not yet know the secret which the Scorpion conceals in the phial at the end of his tail.

1 Or Garden Spiders. Cf. *The Life of the Spider*: chaps. ix to xiv. and appendix.—*Translator's Note.*

2 Cf. *The Life of the Grasshopper*, by J. Henri Fabre, translated by Alexander Teixeira de Mattos: chaps. vi to ix.—*Translator's Note.*

3 Cf. *The Life of the Spider*: chap. xvi.—*Translator's Note.*

4 Cf. *The Life of the Grasshopper*: chap. xviii.—*Translator's Note.*

5 Cf. *idem*: chap. vii.—*Translator's Note.*

6 Cf. *More Hunting Wasps*, by J. Henri Fabre, translated by Alexander Teixeira de Mattos: chap. viii.—*Translator's Note.*

7 The Mantes are the only insects that can turn their heads to right or left. Cf. *The Life of the Grasshopper*: chap. vi.—*Translator's Note.*

8 Cf. *The Life of the Grasshopper*: chaps. xviii and xix.—*Translator's Note.*

9 Cf. *The Life of the Grasshopper*: chap. xviii.—*Translator's Note.*

10 Cf. *The Life of the Grasshopper*: chaps. xiii and xiv.—*Translator's Note.*

11 Cf. *The Life of the Grasshopper*: chaps. xi to xiii.—*Translator's Note.*

12 Cf. *The Life of the Grasshopper*: chaps. i to v.—*Translator's Note.*

13 *Oryctes Nasicornis*, the Rhinoceros Beetle.—*Translator's Note.*

14 *The Glow-worm and Other Beetles*: chap. vii.—*Translator's Note.*

15 The Scarabæi include the Sacred Beetle, the Copris and other Dung-beetles. Cf. *The Sacred Beetle and Others*, by J. Henri Fabre, translated by Alexander Teixeira de Mattos: chaps. i to x.—*Translator's Note.*

16 Or Gold Beetle. Cf. *More Beetles*, by J. Henri Fabre, translated by Alexander Teixeira de Mattos: chaps. xiii and xi.—*Translator's Note.*

17 Or Rose-chafer. Cf. *idem*: chap. i.—*Translator's Note.*

18 Cf. *idem*: chap. ix.—*Translator's Note.*

19 Cf. *The Sacred Beetle and Others*: chaps. xii to xiv.—*Translator's Note.*

20 Cf. *More Beetles*: chap. i.—*Translator's Note.*

21 Cf. *idem*: chaps. xiii and xiv.—*Translator's Note.*

CHAPTER IV
THE LANGUEDOCIAN SCORPION: THE IMMUNITY OF LARVÆ

So little do we possess the Scorpion's secret that unexpected facts crop up that strangely complicate the problem. The study of life brings us these surprises. Repeated experiments, with mutually consistent results, seem to justify our formulation of a rule when, suddenly, important exceptions arise, compelling us to follow a fresh path, directly opposed to the first, and leading us to doubt which is the last stage on the road to knowledge. After labouring long and patiently, like an ox yoked to the plow, we have to plant a note of interrogation at the end of the field which we thought that we had made ready for sowing, without any hope of a final answer. One question leads to another.

To-day the Cetonia-larvæ have forced upon me a similar change of opinion. It was at the end of November, late in the year, when the adult insect was becoming scarce. At this season of dearth, for lack of anything better wherewith to continue my experiments, I thought of resorting to the grubs of the Cetonia, grubs which abound all the year through in a heap of dead leaves in a corner of the enclosure. The naturalist who questions animals is necessarily a torturer: there is no other means of making them speak. A host of questions therefore sends my curiosity rummaging, as a regular thing, in that heap of leaf-mould. Every physiological laboratory has its appointed victims: the Frog, the Guinea-pig, even the Dog. The Cetonia-larva suffices for my rustic work-shop. I add the humble grub to the noble series of victims of whose suffering our knowledge is born.

The advanced and already cold season has not slackened the Scorpion's activity; the fat grub, on its part, in the warm moisture of the decayed leaves, has retained all the suppleness of its back. Both are in perfect condition. I bring them face to face.

The attack is not spontaneous. The larva flees obstinately, turned over on its back, skirting the wall of the cage. The Scorpion remains motionless and looks on; he draws to one side and makes way when the circular track brings the creature in his direction. It is not a prey to his liking, still less a dangerous adversary; and killing merely for killing's sake is not one of his vices. If I did not interfere, the peaceful encounter might continue indefinitely.

I worry the two of them, bring them into contact, irritate them with a bit of a straw, to such good purposes that my devices look like an attack on the part of the grub. The poor topsy-turvy creature is certainly not dreaming of fighting; it is a natural coward which, when in danger, curls up and refuses to move. Unaware of my tricks with the straw, the Scorpion ascribes to his innocent neighbour the annoyance of which I alone am the cause. He waves his sting on high and stabs. The blow has struck home, for the wound bleeds.

Relying on what the adult Cetonia showed me, I expect to see convulsions, the preludes of death. But what is this? When left to itself, the grub uncoils itself and makes off; it travels on its back neither faster nor slower than usual, as though it had not been wounded. Laid on the heap of leaf-mould, it swiftly dives down, without appearing in the least injured. I go to look at it a couple of hours later. It is as vigorous as before the experiment. Its state of health is the same the next day. What are we to make of this rebel? In its adult form, it would have dropped dead; in its larval form, it is indomitable. The wound was deep, since it bleeds, but perhaps the sting omitted to inject any poison, in which case it is a harmless prick, a negligible accident for the sturdy grub. We must try again.

The same subject is stung a second time, by another Scorpion. The result agrees with the first. The wounded grub ambles along on its back entirely at its ease; it dips down into the layer of rotten leaves and quietly resumes eating. The poisoned stab has not affected it.

This immunity cannot be an exceptional instance; there are no privileged individuals among the Cetoniæ; any other subject of the same species ought to prove equally refractory. I unearth twelve larvæ and have them stung, some of them twice or thrice in quick succession. All wriggle a little at the moment when the dirk enters; all lick the bleeding spot if they can reach it with their mouth and then quietly recover from their excitement. They amble along, with their legs in the air; they burrow down into the heart of the leaf-mould. I inspect them next day, the day after and the following days. The poison does not seem to have endangered them in any way.

They look so fit that I conceive a hope of rearing them. In this I succeed to perfection, without further trouble than that of renewing from time to time the provision of rotten leaves. The following year, in June, the twelve that have been subjected to the atrocious sting weave their cocoons and undergo metamorphosis. The Scorpion's stab has caused them no worse damage than a slight itching at the moment when the sting entered the belly.

This curious result reminds me of what Lenz tells us on the subject of the Hedgehog:

"I had a mother Hedgehog," he writes, "who was suckling her young. I threw a large Viper into her box. The Hedgehog soon felt that he was there, for she is guided by the sense of smell and not of sight. She got up, went fearlessly to the Snake and sniffed at him from head to foot, especially about the mouth. The Viper hissed and bit her several times on the snout and lips. As though to make fun of her feeble assailant, she contented herself with licking her wounds, continued her inspection and was once more bitten, but this time in the tongue. At last, she seized the Viper by the head, which she crunched between her jaws, together with the poison-fangs and glands. Then she devoured half the reptile, after which she returned to lie down beside her young and give them to suck. That evening she ate another Viper and what remained of the first. Her health was not affected thereby, nor was that of the little Hedgehogs; her wounds did not even swell.

"Two days later, there was a new Viper and a new fight. The Hedgehog went up to the reptile and smelt it. Opening her jaws and erecting her poison-fangs, the Viper rushed upon her, bit her in the upper lip and remained hanging there for a time. The Hedgehog shook him off and, though bitten ten times in the muzzle and twenty times elsewhere, amidst the prickles, she seized him by the head and devoured him slowly, notwithstanding his contortions. This time again neither the mother nor the sucklings seemed unwell."

It is said that Mithridates, King of Pontus, to fortify his constitution against the dangerous potions with which his enemies attempted to destroy him, accustomed himself to different poisons. By degrees he inured his stomach against venom. Can the Hedgehog, that new Mithridates, in her quality as a Snake-eater, have acquired her immunity by gradual use and wont? Or is it not rather in her case, an original aptitude? When for the first time she bit into the reptile's head, did she not already possess the predisposition necessary to her safety?

She did, the Cetonia-larva tells us for our answer. If any members of the insect clan has to provide itself with defensive means against the Scorpion's attacks, it is certainly not the grub that dwells amid vegetable decay. The two do not frequent the same places, which makes meetings almost impossible. On the larva's part, therefore, there is no increasing tolerance of the poison. The first to find themselves in the Scorpion's presence are perhaps those which I myself place there. Nevertheless, without preparations of any kind, behold the grub refractory to the sting. It possesses, from the first, powers of resistance to the poison which is quite as surprising as that of the reptile-eater.

That the Hedgehog, the appointed exterminator of Vipers, should be endowed with the prerogatives essential to her calling is strictly logical. In the same way, the Bee-eater, the handsomest bird of Mediterranean provinces, crams his crop with impunity with live Wasps; in the same way, the Cuckoo suffers from no irritation when he fills his stomach with a barbed wire entanglement of stinging hairs from the Processionary Caterpillar.1 The function exercised will have it so.

But why need the larva of the Cetonia safeguard itself against the Scorpion, whom she probably never meets? We dare not believe in privileges; rather do we suspect a general aptitude. The Cetonia-larva resists the Scorpion's sting, not as a Cetonia, but as a grub, a preparatory phase on the way to a higher organization. If so, all the larvæ, in a greater or lesser degree, according to their robustness, must possess similar powers of resistance.

What does experiment say on the subject? It behooves us to exempt from the test the weaker grubs, of a delicate constitution. To them a mere prick, without the aid of the poison, would mean a serious and often fatal wound. The point of a needle would gravely injure them. What would it be with the brutal stiletto, even though not poisoned? What we need is a few corpulent grubs which would think little of a perforated belly.

And here I have the very thing I want. An old olive-stump softened underground by decay, provides me with the larva of the Rhinoceros Beetle. It is a plump sausage, as thick as a man's thumb. When stung by the Scorpion, the paunchy grub glides among the scraps of decayed olive-wood with which I have furnished a glass jar; heedless of its mishap, it works its jaws so lustily that, eight months later, having thrived and waxed fat, it is preparing its cell for the metamorphosis. It has passed through the dreadful ordeal unscathed.

As for the adult insect, we have already seen what it does. Stung on the upper surface of the abdomen, under the lifted wing-cases, the colossus soon topples over and feebly kicks its legs about in the air. All movement ceases in three or four days at most. The powerful creature dies; its grub loses nothing in either strength or appetite.

This instance of correct prevision on my part is confirmed by a number of others. In front of my door are two old cherry-laurels, magnificently green at all times of the year. A Capricorn is ruining them for me. This is the little *Cerambyx cerdo*, the usual inhabitant of the hawthorn. The aroma of prussic acid, instead of repelling him, attracts him; the horned dandy is well acquainted with it, thanks to his long experience of the clusters of the hawthorn-blossoms with their searching smell. This alien tree suits him so well for establishing his family that the axe will have to intervene if I want to save what remains.

I cut down the boughs that have suffered most damage. From one limb split into fragments I obtain a dozen of the Capricorn's larvæ. My inspection of the neighbouring hedge-rows provides me with the perfect insect. And now we'll have it out together, O destroyer of my leafy arbour! You shall make amends to me for your misdeeds; you shall die by the Scorpion.

The adults indeed succumb; but the larvæ resist. Lodged in a glass jar, with tiny morsels of the demolished tree, they quietly resume their gnawing. If the provisions do not dry up, the grubs wounded by the Scorpion complete their larval life without accident.

The Capricorn of the Oak, *Cerambyx heros,* behaves in a like fashion. The great horn-wearer perishes; his grub does not mind the sting a jot, for, when restored to its place in the gallery, it tunnels the wood as it did before and completes its development.

The result is the same with the Common Cockchafer. The stabbed insect dies in a few minutes; the White Worm,2 on the contrary, holds out, goes underground and climbs back to the surface to gnaw the lettuce-stalk which I have given it. If my patience as an insect-rearer did not tire, the victim of the accident, from which it quickly recovers, would become a Cockchafer, as may be seen from the paunch sleek and glossy with health.

A near kinsman of the Stag-beetle, *Dorcus parallelopipedus,* whose larva I find in an old tamarisk-stump, adds his evidence to that of the above: the adult insect dies, the larva resists. These instances are sufficient; there is no need to continue on these lines.

Cetonia-, Oryctes-, Capricorn-, Cockchafer- and Dorcus-grubs are fat creatures, addicted to a vegetarian diet. Do these plump larvæ owe their immunity to the nature of their victuals? Or, on the other hand, can the fatty stratum, in which the reserves of these insatiable eaters accumulate, neutralize the virulence of the sting? Let us enquire of some lean flesh-eaters.

I choose the largest of our Ground-Beetles, *Procrusies coriaceus,* a saturnine hunter whom I meet at the foot of the walls, disembowelling a Snail. A bold highwayman and built for fighting, he welds his wing-cases into an inviolable cuirass. I pare away a little of his armour behind, in order to render accessible to the Scorpion's sting the only penetrable part, the upper surface of the abdomen.

We see a repetition of the Gold Beetle's wretched end. The fight against the agonies of the sting would strike us with horror, if things were happening in a higher world. Thus struggles a Dog tortured by the municipal sausage seasoned with strychnine. At first the wounded Beetle scurries off desperately. Suddenly, he stops and raises himself high on his stiffened legs; he lifts his hinder part, lowers his head and supports himself on his mandibles as though about to turn a somersault. A jolt topples him over. He falls; quickly he stands up again and resumes his unnatural attitude. To look at him you would say that his joints were controlled by wires. He is like an automaton worked by a jerky spring. Another shake, another fall, another recovery: and this goes on for twenty minutes or so. At last the demented Beetle collapses on his back and does not get up again, though his limbs continue to move. Next morning he is absolutely motionless.

And what of the larva? Well, though destitute of the layer of fat which would seem to protect the grubs of the Cetonia, the Oryctes and the others, the meagre grub of the Procrustes is so little harmed by the Scorpion's sting that, a fortnight after the ordeal, it buries itself in the ground and digs itself a cell in which the transformation is effected. Lastly, not long after, the adult emerges from the soil in perfect health. Therefore neither the diet nor the degree of stoutness is responsible for this immunity.

Nor is the place occupied in the entomological series, as the Moths will tell us, now that the Beetles have spoken. The first to be questioned is the Zeuzera, whose caterpillar has a calamitous effect upon various trees and shrubs. I take a mother at the moment when she is slipping her long ovipositor into the crevices in the bark of a lilac-tree, to lay her eggs. She is magnificent in her white costume adorned with steel-blue spots.3 I place her at the Scorpion's mercy. The business is not protracted. No sooner is the Zeuzera stung than she dies, with no disordered motions. Death is gentle to her.

And the caterpillar? After the prick, the caterpillar is as well as before. Restored to the gallery whence I extracted it by splitting its lilac-branch, it works away busily as usual: I can see this by the sawdust ejected through the orifice of the cell. The chrysalis and the Moth come in the summer, according to rule.

The Silkworm, which I am able to procure in such numbers as I require from the nurseries at the farms hard by, lends itself much better to experiment. At the end of May, when the rearing is nearly finished, I cause a couple of dozen to be stung. The worms have a fine, chubby skin, into which the sting each time enters easily, producing a copious hemorrhage. The little table on which my curiosity drives me to perpetrate these barbarities is soon covered with splashes of blood like drops of liquid amber.

When restored to their litter of mulberry-leaves, the wounded almost at once set to browsing with their usual appetite. Ten days later, all, from the first to the last, weave their cocoons, which are perfectly normal in shape and thickness. Lastly, from these cocoons, without any losses, emerge Moths whom we shall presently question in another connection. For the moment it is proved that the Silkworm resists the Scorpion's sting. As for the Moth herself, we know what becomes of her. She succumbs slowly, it it true, after the manner of the Great Peacock; but at all events she succumbs: the sting is always fatal.

The Spurge Hawk-moth gives the same answer: the Moth dies quickly: the caterpillar defies the sting, eats its fill and then goes underground itself into a chrysalis under a coarse veil of sand and silk. Nevertheless, among the number operated upon, there are some which are stabbed to death, perhaps because of the multiplicity of their wounds. The skin offers a certain resistance to perforation and the discharge of blood remains uncertain, leaving me undecided as to the efficiency of the stab. I was obliged to prolong the struggle until the evidence was complete and it is probable that I sometimes went too far. The caterpillar which, if pricked but once, would have withstood the ordeal as sturdily as the Silkworm perishes from an overdose.

The mighty, turquoise-bedecked caterpillar of the Great Peacock supplies me with very definite results. When pricked till the blood comes and then replaced on its grazing-ground, the branch of almond, it completes its development and accurately spins its ingenious cocoon.

The Dipteron4 and the Hymenopteron5 should be worth examination. Like the Moth and the Beetle, they undergo a general remoulding through the action of the metamorphosis; but they are small-sized and for the most part could not be easily manipulated were my tweezers to present them to the sting. Their delicate larvæ would die merely of the perforation of the skin. Let us question only the giants.

These latter include various Orthoptera,6 the Tryxalis, the Grey Locust, the White-faced Decticus, the Mole-cricket, the Mantis. As we have already seen, all these succumb when struck by the Scorpion's sting. Now, in their group, the complete development essential to the festival of the pairing is preceded by a transition-form which, without being actually larval, and presenting no likeness whatever to the adult, constitutes an inferior stage, a step towards the marriageable.

The Grey Locust, as we see him on the vine at vintage-time, does not yet possess his magnificent network wings, nor his leathery wing-cases; he possesses only their rudiments, reduced to skimpy coat-tails. The Mole-cricket, who ends by displaying an ample set of wings, which fold back into a sharp tail and enclose the tip of the abdomen, has at first only ungainly stumps, fastened to the upper part of the back.

We behold the same sign of juvenile inferiority in the young Tryxalis, the young Decticus and the others. These mighty, aerial sailing-craft of the future have their canvas enclosed in the germ, in mean-looking sheaths. As for the rest, the insect is, from the beginning, very nearly what it will be in all the fullness of its finery. Age develops and does not transform the Orthopteron.

Now are these incomplete insects, with wing-stumps in the place of wings, are these young insects capable of withstanding the Scorpion's sting as do the true larvæ, the babes of the Oryctes and the Capricorn, the caterpillar of the Hawk-moth and the Bombyx? If the generous sap of youth is an adequate preservative, we ought to find immunity here. We find nothing of the sort. With wings or without, old or young, the Mole-cricket perishes. The Mantis, the Locust, the Tryxalis, whether adult or incomplete, perish likewise.

In the matter of resistance to the Scorpion's poison we are therefore led to class insects in two categories: on the one hand, those which undergo a real transformation, accompanied by an alteration of the whole organism; on the other hand, those which undergo only secondary modifications. In the first division, the larva resists and the adult dies; in the second, death invariably ensues.

What reason can we discover for this difference? Experiment shows us first that resistance to the sting increases as the nature of the victim becomes less highly organized. The Lycosa, the Epeira, the Mantis, all exceedingly sensitive to impressions, succumb on the instant, as though struck by lightning; the Gold Beetle and the Procrustes, those strenuous livers, are seized forthwith with convulsions similar to those produced by strychnine; the Sacred Beetle, a spirited pill-roller, prances in a sort of St. Vitus' dance. On the other hand, the sluggish Oryctes, the lazy Cetonia, both lovers of protracted slumbers in the heart of the roses, bear their misfortunes patiently and fidget feebly for whole days on end before giving up the ghost. Beneath them is the Acridian, the Locust, the essential rustic. Lower still comes the Centipede, an inferior being, roughly organized. It is evident therefore that the venom acts more quickly or more slowly according to the patient's nervous constitution.

Let us consider separately the insects of a superior order, subject to complete transformations. The word metamorphosis applied to them means a change of form. Now is it only the shape that changes when the caterpillar turns into a Moth, or when the grub in the leaf-mould becomes a Cetonia? More than this occurs and much more, as the Scorpion's sting informs us.

A profound and comprehensive renewal is effected in the vital statics of the metamorphosed insect; the substance, which is actually still the same, enters into fusion, subtilizes its atomic structure and becomes liable to sensory vibrations which are the first appanage of the nubile specimen. The armour of the wing-cases, the blades, tufts and quivering stems of the antennæ, the legs fit for running and wings fit for flying: all these are magnificent and yet all these are nothing.

Something else towers high above them. The transformed insect has acquired a new life, more active and richer in sensations. A second birth has taken place in which all is renewed, in the invisible and intangible even more than in the material domain. It is more than a molecular rearrangement; it is the development of aptitudes unknown in the past. The larva, generally a mere scrap of intestine, lived a placid and very monotonous existence and lo, in view of the future instincts, metamorphosis revolutionizes its substance, distils its humours and refines the centres of energy atom by atom. An enormous leap is made towards progress, but the new state has not the sturdy equilibrium of the first, perfection has been gained at the cost of stability; and so the insect dies of an ordeal which the grub would support with impunity.

With the Acridians and the Orthoptera in general, conditions are quite different. Here there is no real metamorphosis, utterly changing the structure, the mode of life and the habits. The insect remains, all its life long, very much what it was on leaving the egg. It is born in a shape which the future will hardly modify, with habits which will not be altered by time. It undergoes no renovation, no sudden growth. In its infancy already it possesses the temperament of the adult; and as such it is deprived of the immunity enjoyed by rudimentary organisms.

Exempted from a probationary period in the grub state, the short-coated Locust suffers from the drawbacks of a too rapid development. He perishes as quickly as the adult, whom he resembles in all but a few details.

I will not deny that the explanation which I have given may not be the right one; and I will not insist upon it. A cast of the net into the depths of the unknown does not always bring up to the surface the correct idea, a very rare catch. A far-reaching fact is acquired nevertheless, even though it remain unexplained. Metamorphosis modifies the organic substance to the degree of changing its innermost properties. The Scorpion's poison, a reagent of transcendental chemistry, distinguishes the flesh of the larva from that of the adult; it is kindly to the first and deadly to the second.

This curious result raises a question which is not alien to the vainglorious theories affecting attenuated viruses, serums and vaccines. A larva subject to complete metamorphosis is stung by the Scorpion; we might readily say that it has been vaccinated, in the sense that it has been inoculated with a virus fatal under the future conditions, but tolerable in its effects in the present stage. The patient does not seem affected by the sting; it begins to eat again and continues its larval work as usual.

The virus, however, cannot fail to act, in one way or another, on the animal's blood or nerves. Might it not lessen the vulnerability which results from the transformation? Can the adult be rendered immune by a habit acquired during the larval stage? Might it be able to resist the virus as Mithridates was able to resist poison? In short, is the insect with a complete metamorphosis whose larva has been stung capable of itself withstanding the sting? That is the question.

The confirmatory arguments are so urgent that we are at first tempted to answer:

"Yes, the adult will resist."

But we will leave experiment to speak for itself. With this object preparations are made with four sets of subjects. The first consists of twelve Cetonia-larvæ, which, after being stung in October, have been revaccinated, that is to say, stung a second time, in May. The second set is also composed of twelve Cetonia-larvæ, but these have been stung once only, in May. Four chrysalids of the Spurge Hawk-moth form the third. They belong to caterpillars stung once, in June. Lastly, I have some cocoons spun by the Silkworm whose vaccination, attended by a flow of blood, I have described above. The Scorpion will once more play his part with each lot after the hatching has taken place.

The Silkworm Moth is the first to respond to my impatience. The Moth is there in two or three weeks' time, bustling about in readiness for the pairing. The stab received as a caterpillar has not cooled his ardour in the very least. I subject him to the test. The attack is laboured and the blow is not clearly struck. No matter: all those attacked perish after a death-struggle lasting a day or two. The previous vaccination has made no difference to the result: they succumbed before and they succumb after.

But these are feeble witnesses, on whom it is not wise to rely. I shall achieve more, I feel convinced, with the Hawk-moths and especially with those sturdy subjects the Cetoniæ. Well, the Hawk-moths whose caterpillars have received the virus which theoretically should render them immune retain their normal vulnerability: when attacked by the sting, they succumb instantly, exactly like the others, who did not at the larval age undergo a preventative inoculation.

Perhaps the number of days elapsing between the stinging of the caterpillar and of the moth was not sufficient to enable the virus to act upon the organism to the requisite degree. It might need a longer space of time to bring about the inward modifications caused by the action of the poison on the insect's organism. The Cetonia-larvæ will perhaps be able to dispense with this period.

I have a set of twelve of them, stung twice over, first in October and then in May. The perfect insect bursts its cocoon at the end of July. Ten months therefore have elapsed since the first sting and three months since the second. Is the adult now immune?

Not at all. When subjected to the Scorpion, my twelve vaccinated specimens all perish, no more and no less quickly than their fellows who were born quietly in their heap of rotten leaves. Twelve others, pricked only once, in May, succumb with the same promptness. In the case of both sets, my devices, which inspired me with confidence at first, miscarry pitifully, to my extreme confusion.

I try another method, that of transfusion of blood, which is related to serotherapy. Since it resists the Scorpion's sting, the larva of the Cetonia must have blood endowed with special qualities, apt to neutralize the virulence of the poison. If transferred from the larva to the adult, might not this blood communicate its qualities and render the perfect insect invulnerable?

I give a Cetonia-grub a superficial wound with the point of a needle. The blood spouts forth abundantly. I collect it in a watch-glass. A glass tube of small diameter, drawn out to a sharp point, serves as an injector. I charge it by suction with the fluid collected, varying the dose from a cubic millimetre to ten and twenty times as much. By blowing into the tube I transfer the liquid into some point of the adult Cetonia, particularly on the ventral surface, where a needle has prepared the way for the fragile injector. The insect stands the operation very well. The richer by a little larval blood and not seriously wounded, it presents every appearance of blooming health.

Now what comes of this treatment? Nothing at all. I wait a day or two to give the injected fluids time to diffuse and act. The Cetonia is then presented to the Scorpion. Veil your face, O foolish physiologist: the creature perishes as it would have done before your presumptuous attempts at surgery. We cannot manipulate animals as we can the reagents of chemistry.

1 Cf. *The Life of the Caterpillar*: chaps. i to vi.—*Translator's Note.*

2 The grub of the Cockchafer.—*Translator's Note.*

3 This is *Z. Æsculi*, also known as the Wood Leopard Moth.—*Translator's Note.*

4 The Diptera are the order of insects comprising the Flies, Mosquitoes, Gnats and Fleas.—*Translator's Note.*

5 The Hymenoptera are the order including the Bees, Wasps, Ants, Ichneumon-flies, Sawflies, Gall-flies, etc.—*Translator's Note.*

6 The order comprising the Grasshoppers, Locusts, Crickets, Cockroaches, Mantes and Earwigs.—*Translator's Note.*

CHAPTER V
THE LANGUEDOCIAN SCORPION: PRELUDES TO THE WEDDING

In April, when the Swallow returns to us and the Cuckoo sounds his first note, a revolution takes place among my hitherto peaceable Scorpions. Several whom I have established in the colony in the enclosure, leave their shelter at nightfall, go wandering about and do not return to their homes. A more serious business: often, under the same stone, are two Scorpions of whom one is in the act of devouring the other. Is this a case of brigandage among creatures of the same order, who, falling into vagabond ways when the fine weather sets in thoughtlessly enter their neighbours' houses and there meet with their undoing unless they be the stronger? One would almost think it, so quickly is the intruder eaten up, for days at a time and in small mouthfuls, even as the usual game would be.

Now here is something to give us a hint. The Scorpions devoured are invariably of middling size. Their lighter colouring, their less protuberant bellies, mark them as males, always males. The others, larger, more paunchy and a little darker in shade, do not end in this unhappy fashion. So these are probably not brawls between neighbours who, jealous of their solitude, would soon settle the hash of any visitor and eat him afterwards, a drastic method of putting a stop to further indiscretions; they are rather nuptial rites, tragically performed by the matron after pairing. To determine how much ground there is for this suspicion is beyond my powers until next year: I am still too badly equipped.

Spring returns once more. I have prepared the large glass cage in advance and stocked it with twenty-five inhabitants, each with his bit of crockery. From mid-April onwards, every evening, when it grows dark, between seven and nine o'clock, great animation reigns in the crystal palace. That which seemed deserted by day now becomes a scene of festivity. As soon as supper is finished, the whole household runs out to look on. A lantern hung outside the panes allows us to follow events.

It is our distraction after the worries of the day; it is our play-house. In this theatre for simple folk, the performances are so highly interesting that, the moment the lantern is lighted, all of us, great and small alike, come and take our places in the stalls; all, down to Tom, the House-dog. Tom, it is true, indifferent to Scorpion affairs, like the true philosopher that he is, lies at our feet and dozes, but only with one eye, keeping the other always open on his friends the children.

Let me try to give the reader an idea of what happens. A numerous assembly soon gathers near the glass panes in the region discreetly lit by the lanterns. Every elsewhere, here, there, single Scorpions walk about and, attracted by the light, leave the shade and hasten to the illuminated festival. The very Moths betray no greater eagerness to flutter to the rays of our lamps. The newcomers mingle with the crowd, while others, tired of their pastimes, withdraw into the shade, snatch a few moments' rest and then impetuously return upon the scene.

These hideous devotees of gaiety provide a dance that is not wholly devoid of charm. Some come from afar: solemnly they emerge from the shadow; then, suddenly, with a rush as swift and easy as a slide, they join the crowd, in the light. Their agility reminds one of Mice scurrying along with their tiny steps. They seek one another and fly precipitately the moment they touch, as though they had mutually burnt their fingers. Others, after tumbling about a little with their play-fellows, make off hurriedly wildly. They take fresh courage in the dark and return.

At times, there is a violent tumult: a confused mass of swarming legs, snapping claws, tails curving and clashing, threatening or fondling, it is hard to say which. In this affray, under favourable conditions, twin specks of light flare and shine like carbuncles. One would take them for eyes that emit flashing glances; in reality they are two polished, reflecting facets, which occupy the front of the head. All, large and small alike, take part in the brawl; it might be a battle to the death, a general massacre; and it is just a wanton frolic. Even so do kittens bemaul each other. Soon, the group disperses; all make off in all sorts of directions, without a scratch, without a sprain.

Behold the fugitives collecting once more beneath the lantern. They pass and pass again; they come and go, often meeting front to front. He who is in the greatest hurry walks over the back of the other, who lets him have his way without any protest but a movement of the body. It is no time for blows: at most, two Scorpions meeting will exchange a cuff, that is to say, a rap of the caudal staff. In their community, this friendly thump, in which the point of the sting plays no part, is a sort of a fisticuff in frequent use. There are better things than entangled legs and brandished tails; there are sometimes poses of the highest originality. Face to face, with claws drawn back, two wrestlers proceed to stand on their heads like acrobats, that is to say, resting only on the fore-quarters, they raise the whole hinder portion of the body, so much so that the chest displays the four little lung pockets uncovered. Then the tails, held vertically erect in a straight line, exchange mutual rubs, gliding one over the other, while their extremities are hooked together and repeatedly fastened and unfastened. Suddenly, the friendly pyramid falls to pieces and each runs off hurriedly, without ceremony.

What were these two wrestlers trying to do, in their eccentric posture? Was it a set-to between two rivals? It would seem not, so peaceful is the encounter. My subsequent observations were to tell me that this was the mutual teasing of a betrothed couple. To declare his flame, the Scorpion stands on his head.

To continue as I have begun and give a homogeneous picture of the thousand tiny particulars gathered day by day would have its advantages: the story would sooner be told; but, at the same time deprived of its details, which vary greatly between one observation and the next and are difficult to piece together, it would be less interesting. Nothing must be neglected in the relation of manners so strange and as yet so little known. At the risk of repeating one's self here and there, it is preferable to adhere to chronological order and to tell the story by fragments, as one's observations reveal fresh facts. Order will emerge from this disorder; for each of the more remarkable evenings supplies some feature that corroborates and completes those which go before. I will therefore continue my narration in the form of a diary.

25th April, 1904.—Hullo! What is this, something I have not yet seen? My eyes, ever on the watch, look upon the affair for the first time. Two Scorpions face each other, with claws outstretched and fingers clasped. It is a question of a friendly grasp of the hand and not the prelude to a battle, for the two partners are behaving to each other in the most peaceful way. There is one of either sex. One is paunchy and browner than the other: this is the female; the other is comparatively slim and pale: this is the male. With their tails prettily curled, the couple stroll with measured steps along the pane. The male is ahead and walks backwards, without jolt or jerk, without any resistance to overcome. The female follows obediently, clasped by her finger-tips and face to face with her leader.

The stroll is interrupted by halts that do not affect the method of conjunction; it is resumed, now here, now there, from end to end of the enclosure. Nothing shows the object which the strollers have in view. They loiter, they dawdle, they most certainly exchange ogling glances. Even so in my village, on Sundays, after vespers, do the youth of both sexes saunter along the hedges, every Jack with his Jill.

Often they tack about. It is always the male who decides which fresh direction the pair shall take. Without releasing her hands, he turns gracefully to the left or right about and places himself side by side with his companion. Then, for a moment, with tail laid flat, he strokes her spine. The other stands motionless, impassive.

For over an hour, without tiring, I watch these interminable comings and goings. A part of the household lends me its eyes in the presence of the strange sight which no one in the world has yet seen, at least with a vision capable of observing. In spite of the lateness of the hour, which upsets all our habits, our attention is concentrated and no essential thing escapes us.

At last, about ten o'clock, something happens. The male has hit upon a potsherd whose shelter seems to suit him. He releases his companion with one hand, with one alone, and continuing to hold her with the other, he scratches with his legs and sweeps with his tail. A grotto opens. He enters and, slowly, without violence, drags the patient Scorpioness after him. Soon both have disappeared. A plug of sand closes the dwelling. The couple are at home.

To disturb them would be a blunder: I should be interfering too soon, at an inopportune moment, if I tried at once to see what was happening below. The preliminary stages may last for the best part of the night; and it does not do for me, who have turned eighty, to sit up so late. I feel my legs giving way; and my eyes seem full of sand.

All night long I dream of Scorpions. They crawl under my bed-clothes, they pass over my face; and I am not particularly excited, so many curious things do I see in my imagination. The next morning, at daybreak, I lift the stoneware. The female is alone. Of the male there is no trace, either in the home or in the neighbourhood. First disappointment, to be followed by many others.

10th May.—It is nearly seven o'clock in the evening; the sky is overcast with signs of an approaching shower. Under one of the potsherds is a motionless couple, face to face, with linked fingers. Cautiously I raise the potsherd and leave the occupants uncovered, so as to study the consequences of the interview at my ease. The darkness of the night falls and nothing, it seems to me, will disturb the calm of the home deprived of its roof. A sharp shower compels me to retire. They, under the lid of the cage, have no need to take shelter against the rain. What will they do, left to their business as they are but deprived of a canopy to their alcove?

An hour later, the rain ceases and I return to my Scorpions. They are gone. They have taken up their abode under a neighbouring tile. Still with their fingers linked, the female is outside and the male indoors, preparing the home. At intervals of ten minutes, the members of my family relieve one another, so as not to lose the exact moment of the pairing, which appears to be imminent. Wasted pains: at eight o'clock, it being now quite dark, the couple, dissatisfied with the spot, set out on a fresh ramble, hand in hand, and go prospecting elsewhere. The male, walking backwards, leads the way, chooses the dwelling as he pleases; the female follows with docility. It is an exact repetition of what I saw on the 25th of April.

At last a tile is found to suit them. The male goes in first but this time neither hand releases his companion for a moment. The nuptial chamber is prepared with a few sweeps of the tail. Gently drawn towards him, the Scorpioness enters in the wake of her guide.

I visit them a couple of hours later, thinking that I've given them time enough to finish their preparations. I lift the potsherd. They are there in the same posture, face to face and hand in hand. I shall see no more to-day.

The next day, nothing new either. Each sits confronting the other, meditatively. Without stirring a limb, the gossips, holding each other by the finger-tips, continue their endless interview under the tile. In the evening, at sunset, after sitting linked together for four-and-twenty hours, the couple separate. He goes away from the tile, she remains; and matters have not advanced by an inch.

This observation gives us two facts to remember. After the stroll to celebrate the betrothal, the couple need the mystery and quiet of a shelter. Never would the nuptials be consummated in the open air, amid the bustling crowd, in sight of all. Remove the roof of the house, by night or day, with all possible discretion; and the husband and wife, who seem absorbed in meditation, march off in search of another spot. Also, the sojourn under the cover of a stone is a long one: we have just seen it spun out to twenty-four hours and even then without a decisive result.

12th May.—What will this evening's sitting teach us? The weather is calm and hot, favourable to nocturnal pastimes. A couple has been formed: how things began I do not know. This time the male is greatly inferior to his corpulent mate. Nevertheless, the skinny wight performs his duty gallantly. Walking backwards, according to rule, with his tail rolled trumpetwise, he marches the fat Scorpioness around the glass ramparts. After one circuit follows another, sometimes in the same, sometimes in the opposite direction.

Pauses are frequent. Then the foreheads touch, bend a little to left and right, as if the two were whispering in each other's ears. The little fore-legs flutter in feverish caresses. What are they saying to each other? How shall we translate their silent epithalamium into words?

The whole household turns out to see this curious team, which our presence in no way disturbs. The pair are pronounced to be "pretty"; and the expression is not exaggerated. Semitranslucent and shining in the light of the lantern, they seem carved out of a block of amber. Their arms outstretched, their tails rolled into graceful spirals, they wander on with a slow movement and with measured tread.

Nothing puts them out. Should some vagabond, taking the evening air and keeping to the wall like themselves, meet them on their way, he stands aside—for he understands these delicate matters—and leaves them a

free passage. Lastly, the shelter of a tile receives the strolling pair, the male entering first and backwards: that goes without saying. It is nine o'clock.

The idyll of the evening is followed, during the night, by a hideous tragedy. Next morning, we find the Scorpioness under the potsherd of the previous day. The little male is by her side, but slain, and more or less devoured. He lacks the head, a claw, a pair of legs. I place the corpse in the open, on the threshold of the home. All day long, the recluse does not touch it. When night returns, she goes out and, meeting the deceased on her passage, carries him off to a distance to give him a decent funeral, that is to finish eating him.

This act of cannibalism agrees with what the open-air colony showed me last year. From time to time, I would find, under the stones, a pot-bellied female making a comfortable ritual meal off her companion of the night. I suspected that the male, if he did not break loose in time, once his functions were fulfilled, was devoured, wholly or partly, according to the matron's appetite. I now have the certain proof before my eyes. Yesterday, I saw the couple enter their home after their usual preliminary, the stroll; and, this morning, under the same tile, at the moment of my visit, the bride is consuming her mate.

Well, one supposes that the poor wretch has attained his ends. Were he still necessary to the race, he would not be eaten yet. The couple before us have therefore been quick about the business, whereas, I see that others fail to finish after provocations and contemplations exceeding in duration the time which it takes the hour-hand to go twice around the clock. Circumstances impossible to state with precision—the condition of the atmosphere perhaps, the electric tension, the temperature, the individual ardour of the couple—to a large extent accelerate or delay the finale of the pairing; and this constitutes a serious difficulty for the observer anxious to seize the exact moment whereat the as yet uncertain function of the combs might be revealed.

14th May.—It is certainly not hunger that stirs up my animals night after night. The quest of food has nothing to say to their evening rounds. I have served to the busy crowd a varied bill of fare, selected from that which they appear to like best. It includes tender morsels in the shape of young Locusts; small Grasshoppers, fleshier than the Acridians; Moths minus their wings. At a later season, I add Dragon-flies, a highly-appreciated dish, as is proved by their equivalent, the full-grown Ant-lion, of whom I used to find the remnants, the wings, in the Scorpion's cave.

This luxurious game leaves them indifferent; they pay no attention to it. Amid the hubbub, the Locusts hop, the Moths beat the ground with the stumps of their wings, the Dragon-flies quiver; and the Scorpions pass. They tread them underfoot, they topple them over, they push them aside with a stroke of the tail; in short, they absolutely refuse to look at them. They have other business in hand.

Almost all of them skirt the glass wall. Some of them obstinately attempt to scale it: they hoist themselves on their tails, fall down, try again elsewhere. With their outstretched fists they knock against the pane; they want to get away at all costs. And yet the grounds are large enough, there is room for all; the walks lend themselves to long strolls. No matter: they want to roam afar. If they were free, they would disperse in every direction. Last year, at the same time, the colonists of the enclosure left the village and I never saw them again.

The spring pairing-season forces them to set forth exploring. The shy hermits of yesterday now leave their cells and go on love's pilgrimage; heedless of food, they go in quest of their kind. Among the stones of their domain there must be choice spots at which meetings take place, at which assemblies are held. If I were not afraid of breaking my legs, at night, over the rocky obstacles of their hills, I should love to assist at their matrimonial festivals, amid the delights of liberty. What do they do up there, on their bare slopes? Much the same, apparently, as in the glass enclosure. Having picked a bride, they take her about, for a long stretch of time, hand in hand, through the tufts of lavender. If they miss the attractions of my lantern, they have the moon, that incomparable lamp, to light them.

20th May.—The sight of the first invitation to a stroll is not an event upon which we can count every evening. Several emerge from under their stones already linked in couples. In this concatenation of clasped fingers, they have passed the whole day, motionless, face to face, meditating. When night comes, without separating for a moment, they resume the walk around the glass begun on the evening before, or even earlier. No one knows when or how the junction was effected. Others meet unexpectedly in sequestered passages, difficult of inspection. By the time that I see them, it is too late: the team is on the way.

To-day, chance favours me. The acquaintance is made before my eyes, in the full light of the lantern. A frisky, sprightly male, in his hurried rush through the crowd, suddenly finds himself confronting a fair passer-by who takes his fancy. She does not gainsay him; and things move quickly.

The foreheads touch, the claws engage; the tails swing with a spacious gesture: they stand up vertically, hook together at the tips and softly stroke each other with a slow caress. The two animals stand on their heads in the manner already described. Soon, the raised bodies sink to the ground; fingers are clasped and the couple start on their stroll without more ado. The pyramidal pose, therefore, is really the prelude to the harnessing. The pose, it is true, is not rare between two individuals of the same sex on the meeting; but it is then less correct and above all, less marked by ceremony. At such times, we find movements of impatience, instead of friendly excitations; the tails strike in lieu of fondling each other.

Let us watch the male, who hurries away backwards, very proud of his conquest. Other females are met, who stand around and look on inquisitively, perhaps enviously. One of them flings herself upon the ravished bride, clasps her with her legs and makes an effort to stop the team. The male exhausts himself in attempts to overcome this resistance; in vain he shakes, in vain he pulls: things won't move. Undistressed by the accident, he throws up the game. A neighbour is there, close by. Cutting parley short, this time without any further declaration, he takes her hands and invites her to a stroll. She protests, releases herself and runs away.

From among the group of onlookers, a second is solicited, in the same free and easy manner. She accepts, but there is nothing to tell us that she will not escape from her seducer on the way. But what does the coxcomb care? There are more where she came from! And what does he want, when all is said? The first that comes along!

This first-comer he soon finds, for here he is, leading his conquest by the hand. He passes into the belt of light. Exerting all his strength, he tugs and jerks at the other if she refuses to come, but is gentle in his manner when he obtains a docile obedience. Pauses, sometimes rather prolonged, are frequent.

Then the male indulges in some curious exercises. Bringing his claws, or let us say, his arms towards him and then stretching them out again, he compels the female to make a like alternation of movements. The two of them form a system of jointed rods, like a lazy-tongs, opening and closing their quadrilateral by turns. After this gymnastic exercise, the mechanism contracts and remains stationary.

The foreheads now touch; the two mouths come together with tender effusions. The word "kisses" comes to one's mind to express these caresses. It is not applicable; for head, face, lips, cheeks, all are missing. The animal, lopped off short, as though with the shears, has not even a muzzle. Where we look for a face we are confronted with a dead wall of hideous jaws.

And to the Scorpion this represents the supremely beautiful! With his fore-legs, more delicate, more agile than the others, he pats the horrible mask, which in his eyes is an exquisite little face; voluptuously he nibbles and tickles with his jaws the equally hideous mouth opposite. It is all superb in its tenderness and simplicity. The Dove is said to have invented the kiss. But I know that he had a fore-runner in the Scorpion.

Dulcinea lets her admirer have his way and remains passive, not without a secret longing to slip off. But how is she to set about it? It is quite easy. The Scorpioness makes a cudgel of her tail and brings it down with a bang upon the wrists of her too-ardent wooer, who there and then lets go. The match is broken off, for the time being. To-morrow, the sulking-fit will be over and things will resume their course.

25th May.—This blow of the cudgel teaches us that the docile companion revealed by our first observations is capable of whims, of obstinate refusals, of sudden divorces. Let us give an example.

This evening, he and she, a seemly couple, are out for a stroll. A tile is found and appears to suit. Letting go with one claw, so as to have some freedom of action, the male works with his legs and tail to clear the entrance. He goes in. By degrees, as the dwelling is dug out, the female follows him, meekly and gently, so one would think.

Soon, the place and time perhaps not suiting her, she reappears and half-emerges, backwards. She struggles against her abductor, who, on his side, pulls her to him, without, as yet, showing himself. A lively contest ensues, one making every effort outside the cabin, the other inside. They go backwards and forwards by turns; and success is undecided. At last, with a sudden effort, the Scorpioness drags her companion out.

The unbroken team is in the open; the walk is resumed. For a good hour, they hug the panes, tacking down one side of the cage and back by the other and then return to the tile recently deserted, the exact same one. As the way is already open, the male enters without delay and pulls like mad. Outside, the Scorpioness resists. Stiffening her legs, which plough the soil, and buttressing her tail against the arch of the tile, she refuses to go in. I like this resistance. What would the pairing be without the playful setting of the preliminaries?

Under the stone, however, the ravisher insists and contrives to such good purpose that the rebel obeys. She enters. It has just struck ten. If I have to sit up for the rest of the night, I will wait for the result; I shall turn over the potsherd at the fitting moment to catch a glimpse of what is happening underneath. Good opportunities are rare: let us make the most of this one. What shall I see?

Nothing at all. In half an hour or less, the recalcitrant female frees herself, comes out of the shelter and flees. The other at once hurries up from the back of the cabin, stops on the threshold and looks out. The beauty has escaped him. Sheepishly he returns indoors. He has been cheated. So have I.

CHAPTER VI
THE LANGUEDOCIAN SCORPION: THE PAIRING

June sets in. For fear of a disturbance caused by too brilliant an illumination, I have hitherto kept the lantern hung outside, at some distance from the pane. The insufficient light does not allow me to observe certain details of the manner in which the couple are linked when strolling. Do they both play an active part in the scheme of the clasped hands? Are their fingers mutually interlinked? Or is only one of the pair active; and, if so, which? Let us ascertain exactly; the thing is not without importance.

I place the lantern inside, in the centre of the cage. There is good light everywhere. Far from being scared, the Scorpions are gayer than ever. They come hurrying round the beacon; some even try to climb up, so as to be nearer the flame. They succeed in doing so by means of the framework containing the glass panes. They hang on to the edges of the tin strips and stubbornly, heedless of slipping, end by reaching the top. There, motionless, lying partly on the glass, partly on the support of the metal casing, they gaze the whole evening long, fascinated by the burning wick. They remind me of the Great Peacock Moths that used to hang in ecstasy under the reflector of my lamp.1

At the foot of the beacon, in the full light, a couple lose no time in standing on their heads. The two fence prettily with their tails and then go a strolling. The male alone acts. With the two fingers of each claw, he has seized the two fingers of the corresponding claw of the Scorpioness bundled together. He alone exerts himself and squeezes; he alone is at liberty to break the team when he likes: he has but to open his pincers. The female cannot do this; she is a prisoner, handcuffed by her ravisher.

In rather infrequent cases, one may see even more remarkable things. I have caught the Scorpion dragging his sweetheart along by the two forearms; I have seen him pull her by one leg and the tail. She had resisted the advances of the outstretched hand; and the bully, forgetful of all reserve, had thrown her on her side and clawed hold of her at random. The thing is quite clear: we have to do with a regular rape, abduction with violence. Even so did Romulus' youths rape the Sabine women.

The brutal ravisher is singularly persistent in his feats of prowess, when we remember that things end tragically sooner or later. The ritual demands that he shall be eaten after the wedding. What a strange world, in which the victim drags the sacrificer by main force to the altar!

From one evening to the next, I become aware that the more corpulent females in my menagerie hardly ever take part in the sport of the linked team; it is nearly always the young, slim-waisted ones to whom the ardent strollers pay their addresses. They must have sprightly flappers. True, there are moments when they have interviews with the others, accompanied by strokes of the tail and attempts at harnessing; but these are brief displays, devoid of any great fervour. No sooner is she seized by the fingers than the portly temptress, with a blow of her tail, rebukes the untimely familiarity. The rejected suitor retires from the contest without insisting further. They go their several ways.

The big-bellied ones are therefore elderly matrons, indifferent nowadays to the effusive manners of the pairing-season. This time last year and perhaps even before, they had their own good spell; and that is enough for them henceforth. The female Scorpion's period of gestation is consequently extraordinarily long, longer than will be often found even among animals of a higher order. It takes her a year or more to mature her germs.

Let us return to the couple whom we have just seen forming up beneath the lantern. I inspect them at six o'clock the next morning. They are under the tile linked precisely as though for a stroll, that is to say, face to face and with clasped fingers. While I watch them, a second pair forms and begins to wander to and fro. The early hour of the expedition surprises me: I had never seen such an incident in broad daylight and was seldom to see it again. As a rule it is at nightfall that the Scorpions go strolling in couples. Whence this hurry to-day?

I seem to catch a glimpse of the reason. It is stormy weather; in the afternoon, there is incessant, very mild thunder. St. Mèdard, whose feast fell yesterday, is opening his flood-gates wide; it pours all night. The great electric tension and the smell of ozone have stirred up the sleepy hermits, who, nervously irritated, for the most part come to the threshold of their cells, stretching their questioning claws outside and enquiring into the condition of things. Two, more violently excited than the others, have come out, influenced by the intoxication of the pairing which is enhanced by the intoxication of the storm; they suited each other; and here they are solemnly marching to the sound of the thunder-claps.

They pass before open huts and try to go in. The owner objects. He appears in the doorway, shaking his fists, and his action seems to say:

"Go somewhere else; this place is taken."

They go away. They meet with the same refusal at other doors, the same threats from the occupant. At last, for want of anything better, they make their way under the tile where the first couple have been lodging since the day before.

The cohabitation entails no quarrelling; the first settlers and the newcomers, side by side, keep very quiet, each couple absorbed in meditation, completely motionless, with fingers still clasped. And this goes on all day. At five o'clock in the evening, the couples separate. Anxious apparently to take part in the usual twilight rejoicings, the males leave the shelter; the females, on the other hand, remain under the tile. Nothing, so far as I know, has happened during the long interview, nothing despite the stimulating effects of the thunderstorm.

This fourfold occupation of one dwelling is not an isolated instance: groups, regardless of sex, are not infrequent under the potsherds in the glass cage. I have already said that, in their original homes, I have never found two Scorpions under one stone. We must not infer from this that unsociable habits prohibit all intercourse among neighbours; we should be making a mistake: the glazed enclosure tells us so. There are cabins in more than sufficient numbers; each Scorpion would be able to choose himself a dwelling and thenceforth to occupy it as the jealous owner. Nothing of the kind takes place. Once the nocturnal excitement sets in, there is no such thing as a home respected by others. Everything is common property. Whoever wishes to slip under the first tile that offers does so without protest from the occupant. The Scorpions go abroad, walk about and enter any house they may chance upon. In this way, when the twilight diversions are over, groups of three, four, or sometimes more are formed without distinction of sex and, packed pretty closely in the narrow home, spend the rest of the night and the whole of the following day together. For that matter, theirs is only a temporary shanty, which is exchanged next evening for another, according to the strollers' fancy. And these roving gipsies live quite peaceably. There is never any serious strife between them, even when they are five or six in the same messroom.

Now this tolerance prevails only in the adults, due, no doubt, to some degree, to the fear of reprisals. There is another and more imperative reason for peaceful relations: concord is a necessity in assemblies at which the future is being prepared. The Scorpions' characters therefore become assuaged, but not entirely: there are always perverse appetites among the females who are about to enter upon the period of gestation.

I have always present in my mind the memory of the following odious spectacles. A heedless male, who has attained hardly a third or a fourth of his final size, is passing, unthinking, of evil, before the door of a dwelling.

The fat matron comes out, accosts the poor wretch, picks him up in her claws, kills him with her sting and then quietly eats him.

Scorpion lads and lasses, the one sooner, the other later, perish in the same manner in the glass cage. I scruple to replace the deceased: it would be providing fresh food for the slaughter. There were a dozen of them; and in a few days I have not one left. Without the excuse of hunger, for the regular victuals are plentiful, the females have devoured them all. Youth is certainly a beautiful thing, but it has terrible drawbacks in the society of these ogresses.

I would gladly ascribe these massacres to the peculiar cravings often provoked by pregnancy. The future mother is suspicious and intolerant; to her everything is an enemy, to be got rid of by eating it, when strength permits. And indeed, when the quickly emancipated family is born, in the middle of August, a profound peace reigns in the menagerie. My vigilance is unable to surprise a single case of these outbreaks of cannibalism which used to occur so often.

On the other hand, the males, indifferent to the safety of the family, know nothing of these tragic frenzies. They are peaceful creatures, blunt in their manners, but in any event incapable of ripping up their fellows. We never see two rivals disputing in mortal combat, for the possession of the coveted bride. Things happen, if not mildly, at least without blows of the dagger.

Two suitors come upon the same Scorpioness. Which of the two will propose to her and take her for a walk? The point will be decided by strength of wrist.

Each takes the beauty by the hand nearest to him with the fingers of one claw. One standing on the right, the other on the left, they pull with all their might in opposite directions. The legs, braced backwards, exert a powerful leverage; the flanks quiver; the tails sway to and fro and suddenly dart forward. Now for it! They tug at the Scorpioness by fits and starts with sudden backward runs; it is as though they meant to pull her in two and each to carry off a piece. A declaration of love implies a threat to rend her asunder.

On the other hand, there is no direct exchange of fisticuffs between them, not even a back-hander with the tail. Only the victim is ill-treated and roughly at that. To see these lunatics struggling, you would think that their arms would be torn out. Nevertheless, there are no dislocations.

Weary of an ineffectual contest, the two competitors at last take each other by the hands that remain at liberty: they form a chain of three and resume the process of jerking and tugging more violently than ever. Each of them bustles to and fro, advances, recoils and pulls his hardest till he is exhausted. Suddenly, the more fatigued of the two throws up the sponge and runs away, leaving his adversary in possession of the object of their passions so vehemently disputed. Then, with his free claw, the victor completes the team and the stroll begins. As for the vanquished, we will not trouble about him: he will soon have found something in the crowd to make amends for his confusion.

I will give you another instance of these meek encounters between rivals. A couple are walking along. The male is of medium size, but nevertheless very eager at the game. When his companion refuses to advance, he pulls at her with jerks which send shudders along his spine. A second male, larger than the first, appears upon the scene. The lady takes his fancy; he desires her. Will he abuse his strength, fling himself on the little chap, beat him, perhaps stab him? By no means. Among Scorpions these delicate matters are not decided by force of arms.

The burly fellow leaves the dwarf alone. He goes straight to the coveted fair and seizes her by the tail. Then the two vie with each other in pulling, one in front, the other behind. A brief contest follows, leaving each of them the master of a claw. With frantic violence, one works on the right, the other on the left, as though they wished to pull the dame to pieces. At length the smaller realizes that he is beaten; he lets go and makes off. The big one lays hold of the abandoned prey; and the team takes the road without further incident.

Thus, evening after evening, for four months, from the end of April to the beginning of September, the preludes to the pairing are indefatigably repeated. The scorching dog-days do not calm these unruly lovers; on the contrary, they inflame them with new ardour. In the spring, I used to surprise the pilgrims' tandems singly, at long intervals; in July I observe them by threes and fours at a time, on the same evening.

I take the opportunity, with not much success, to enquire what goes on under the tiles where the strolling couples take refuge; my wish is to see the details of the tender interview from start to finish. It does me no good to turn over the potsherd, even during the quiet hours of the night. I have tried often and in vain. When deprived of their roof, the linked couples resume their ramble and make for another shelter, where the impossibility of prolonged observation obtains once more. Special circumstances, independent of any intervention on our part, are needed to make the delicate undertaking succeed.

To-day these circumstances are present. At seven o'clock in the morning, on the 3rd of July, a couple attracts my attention, a couple whom I saw forming, walking about and selecting a home on the previous evening. The male is under the tile, quite invisible save for the tips of his claws. The cabin was too small to shelter the two. He went in; she, with her mighty paunch, remained outside, clutched by the fingers by her companion.

The tail, curved into a wide arc, is bent slackly to one side, with the point of the sting resting on the ground. The eight legs, firmly planted, are drawn backwards, marking a tendency to escape. The whole body is completely motionless. I inspect the fat Scorpioness twenty times in the course of the day, without perceiving the least movement of the hinder part, the least change in the attitude, the least flexion in the curve of the tail. The animal could be no more lifeless if turned to stone.

The male, on his side, is no more active. Though I cannot see him, I at least observe his fingers, which would tell me of any change of posture. And this petrified condition, which has lasted for the best part of the night, persists all day, until eight o'clock in the evening. What do they feel, facing each other thus? What are they doing, motionless with clasped fingers? If the expression were allowable, I should say that they are meditating profoundly. It is the only term that more or less represents what I see. But no human language could have words fit to convey the bliss, the ecstasy of the Scorpions thus coupled by the finger-tips. Let us remain silent upon that which we cannot possibly understand.

A little before eight o'clock, when the animation outside the house is already approaching its height, the female suddenly moves; she struggles and, with an effort, contrives to release herself. She flees, with one of the pincers bent back towards her and the other stretched out. To break her seductive bonds, she pulled with such violence that she put one of her shoulders out of joint. She flees, feeling her way with the uninjured claw. The male runs off too. All is over for this evening.

These rambles in pairs, which are customary in the evening all through the summer, are evidently the preliminaries to more serious affairs. The strollers inspect each other, display their graces, show off their qualities before coming to conclusions. But when does the decisive moment arrive? My patience is exhausted in waiting for it; I vainly prolong my vigils and turn over potsherd after potsherd, in my anxiety at last to know the exact part played by the combs; my hopes remain unfulfilled.

It is at a very late hour in the night that the marriage is consummated: of that I have no doubt whatever. If I had any chance of arriving at the right moment, I would struggle against sleep till break of day: my old eyelids are still capable of doing so when the acquisition of an idea is at stake. But how hazardous my perseverance would be!

I am very well aware, having seen it over and over again, that, in the vast majority of cases, we find the couple next morning, under the tile, harnessed together just as they were on the evening before. To succeed, I should have to upset the habits of a lifetime and lie in wait every night for three or four months on end. The plan is beyond my strength: and I give it up.

Once only did I obtain an inkling of the solution of the problem. At the moment when I lift the stone, the male is turning over without releasing the clasp of his hands; with his belly upturned, he slowly slides backwards under his mate.2 Even so does the Cricket behave when his pleadings at last obtain a hearing. In this posture, the couple would only have to steady themselves, probably with the teeth of their combs, to achieve their ends. But, startled by the violation of their home, the superimposed twain separate then and there. From the little that I have seen, it seems likely, therefore, that the Scorpions end their mating in an attitude similar to that of the Crickets. In addition they have their hands clasped and their combs interlocked.

I am better informed of subsequent events within the cell. Let us mark the tiles under which the couples take refuge in the evening, after their stroll. What do we find next morning? As a rule, precisely the same linked couple as the day before, face to face, with fingers united.

Sometimes the female is alone. The male, having finished his business, has found means to release himself and go away. He had grave reasons for cutting short the transports of the alcove. Especially in May, the time of the most ardent enjoyment, I often indeed find the female nibbling and relishing her deceased mate.

Who committed the murder? The Scorpioness, evidently. These are the atrocious customs of the Praying Mantis:3 the lover is stabbed and then eaten, if he does not retire in time. By the exercise of nimbleness and decision, he can do so sometimes, not always. He is able to release his hands, for it is his that squeeze; by lifting his thumbs, he unclasps them. But there remains the diabolical little mechanism of the combs, an apparatus of sensual pleasure, now a trap. On both sides the long teeth of this interlocking gear, closely fitting and perhaps spasmodically contracted, refuse to come apart as promptly as could be wished. The poor fellow is lost.

He has a poisoned dagger similar to that which threatens him: can he, does he know how to defend himself? It seems as though he cannot, for he is always the victim. It is possible that his reversed posture hinders him in wielding his tail, which he must curve over his back if he wishes to bring it into play. Perhaps also an insuperable instinct prevents him from putting the future mother to death. He allows himself to be pinked by the terrible bride; he perishes without defence.

The widow forthwith begins to eat him. It is a part of the ritual, as with the Spiders, who, deprived of the Scorpion's fatal engine, at least leave the males time to escape if they are prompt enough in forming a decision.

The funeral repast, though frequent, is not indispensable; whether the male is devoured depends a little on the condition of the female's stomach. I have seen some who, despising the nuptial morsel, frugally swallowed the head of the deceased and then flung the corpse outside, without touching it again. I have seen these furies carry their dead husband at arm's length, dragging him about the whole morning, in sight of all, like a trophy, and then, without further ceremony, leaving him untouched and abandoning him to those eager dissectors, the Ants.

1 Cf. *The Life of the Caterpillar*: chap. xi.—*Translator's Note.*

2 Cf. *The Life of the Grasshopper*: chap. xvi.—*Translator's Note.*

3 Cf. *idem*: chap. vii.—*Translator's Note.*

CHAPTER VII THE LANGUEDOCIAN SCORPION: THE FAMILY

Book-knowledge is a poor resource in the problems of life; assiduous study with the facts is preferable in this connection to the best stocked library. In many cases, ignorance is a good thing: the mind retains its freedom of investigation and does not stray along the roads leading nowhither, suggested by one's reading. I have proved the truth of this once more.

An anatomical monograph had told me that the Languedocian Scorpion is big with young in September. Although it was written by a master's hand, how much better should I have done not to consult it! The family sees the light of day long before this season, at least in my climate; and, as the rearing lasts but a short time, I should have seen nothing had I delayed until September. A third year of observation, tiresome to wait for, would have become necessary, in order at last to witness a sight which I foresaw to be of the highest interest. But for exceptional circumstances, I should have allowed the fleeting opportunity to pass, and should have lost a year and perhaps even abandoned the subject.

Yes, ignorance may have its advantages; the new is found far from the beaten track. One of our most illustrious masters, little suspecting the lesson he was giving me, taught me that some time ago. One fine day, Pasteur1 rang unexpectedly at my front-door: the very same man who was soon to acquire such world-wide celebrity. His name was familiar to me. I had read the scholar's fine work on the dissymmetry of tartaric acid; I had followed with the greatest interest his researches on the theory of spontaneous generation.

Each period has its scientific crotchet: to-day, it is evolution; in those days, it was spontaneous generation. With his glass bulbs made sterile or fertile at will, with his experiments which were magnificent in their severity and simplicity, Pasteur gave the death-blow to the lunacy which professed to see life springing from a chemical conflict in the seat of putrefaction.

At this time, the dispute, which was to be so triumphantly elucidated, was at its height. I welcomed my distinguished visitor to the best of my ability. The scientist had come to me before all others for certain particulars. I owed this signal honour to my quality of fellow physicist and chemist. Such a poor, obscure, fellow scientist!

Pasteur's tour through the Avignon region had sericiculture for its object. For some years, the Silk-worm-nurseries had been in confusion, ravaged by unknown plagues. The worms, for no appreciable reason, were falling into a putrid deliquescence, and then hardening, so to speak, into plaster sugar-plums. The downcast peasant saw one of his chief crops disappearing; after great trouble and expense, he had to fling his nurseries on the dust-heap.

A few words were exchanged on the prevailing blight; and then, without further preamble, my visitor said:

"I should like to see some cocoons. I have never seen any; I know them only by name. Could you get me some?"

"Nothing easier. My landlord happens to sell cocoons; and he lives in the next house. If you will wait a moment, I will bring you what you want."

Four steps took me to my neighbour's, where I crammed my pockets with cocoons. I came back and handed them to the savant. He took one; he turned and turned it between his fingers; he examined it curiously, as one would a strange object from the other end of the world. He put it to his ear and shook it.

"Why, it makes a noise!" he said, quite surprised. "There's something inside!"

"Of course there is."

"What is it?"

"The chrysalis."

"How do you mean, the chrysalis?"

"I mean the sort of mummy into which the caterpillar changes before becoming a Moth."

"And has every cocoon one of those things inside it?"

"Obviously. It is to protect the chrysalis that the caterpillar spins."

"Really!"

And without more words, the cocoons passed into the pocket of the savant, who was to instruct himself at his leisure touching that great novelty, the chrysalis. I was struck by this magnificent assurance. Pasteur had come to regenerate the Silkworm, while knowing nothing about caterpillars, cocoons, chrysalids or metamorphoses. The ancient gymnasts came naked to the fight. The talented combatant of the plague of our Silk-worm-nurseries hastened to the battle likewise naked, that is to say, destitute of the simplest notions about the insect which he was to deliver from danger. I was staggered; nay, more, I was thunderstruck.

I was not so much amazed by what followed. Pasteur was occupied at the time with another question, that of the improvement of wine by heating. Suddenly changing the conversation,

"Show me your cellar," he said.

I! I show my cellar, my private cellar, poor I, lately, with my pitiful teacher's salary, could not allow myself the luxury of a little wine and used to make a sort of small cider by setting a handful of brown sugar and some grated apples to ferment in a jar! My cellar! Show my cellar! Why not my barrels, my cobwebbed bottles, each labelled with its year and quality! My cellar!

Full of confusion, I evaded the request and tried to change the subject. But he persisted:

"Show me your cellar, please."

There was no resisting such firmness. I pointed with my finger to a corner in the kitchen, where stood a chair with no seat to it and, on that chair, a demijohn containing two or three gallons.

"That's my cellar, sir."

"Is that your cellar?"

"I have no other."

"Is that all?"

"Yes, that's all, I'm sorry to say."

"Really!"

Not a word more; nothing further from the savant. Pasteur, it was evident, had never tasted the highly-spiced dish which the vulgar call *la vache enragée*. Though my cellar—the dilapidated chair and the more than half-empty demijohn—had nothing to tell of the fermentation to be checked by heat, it spoke eloquently of another thing which my illustrious visitor seemed not to understand. There was one microbe that escaped his notice, and a very terrible microbe: that of ill-fortune strangling good-will.

In spite of the unlucky introduction of the cellar, I am none the less struck by his serene assurance. He knows nothing of the transformation of insects; he has just seen a cocoon for the first time and learnt that there is something inside that cocoon, the rough draft of the moth that will be; he is ignorant of what is known to the meanest schoolboy of our southern province; and this novice, whose artless questions surprise me so greatly, is about to revolutionize the hygiene of the Silk-worm nurseries. In the same way, he will revolutionize medicine and general hygiene.

His weapon is theory, heedless of details, and taking a bird's-eye view of the whole question. What cares he for metamorphoses, larvæ, nymphs, cocoons, pupæ, chrysalids and the thousand and one little secrets of entomology! For the purposes of his problem, perhaps, it is just as well to be ignorant of all that. His theories will retain their independence and their daring flight all the more easily; their movements will be all the freer, when released from the leading-strings of the known.

Encouraged by the magnificent example of the cocoons rattling in Pasteur's astonished ears, I have made it a rule to adopt the method of ignorance in my investigations of the instincts. I read very little. Instead of turning the pages of books, an expensive proceeding quite beyond my means, instead of consulting other people, I persist in obstinately interviewing my subject until I succeed in making him speak. I know nothing. So much the better: my queries will be all the freer, now in this direction, now in the opposite, according to the glimpses of light obtained. And if, by chance, I do open a book, I take care to leave a compartment of my mind wide open to doubt; for the soil which I am clearing bristles with weeds and brambles.

For lack of taking this precaution, I very nearly wasted a year. Relying on what I had read, I did not look for the family of the Languedocian Scorpion until September; and I obtained it quite unexpectedly in July. The difference between the real and the anticipated date I ascribe to the disparity of the climates: my observations were all made in Provence and my informant, Lóon Dufour,2 made his in Spain. Notwithstanding the master's high authority, I ought to have been on my guard. I was not; and I should have lost the opportunity if, as luck would have it, the Common Black Scorpion had not taught me. Ah, how right was Pasteur not to know the chrysalis!

The Common Scorpion, smaller and much less active than the other, was reared, for purposes of comparison, in some humble glass jam-pots standing on the table in my study. These unassuming receptacles did not take up much room and were easy to examine and I made a point of visiting them daily. Every morning, before sitting down to blacken a few pages of my diary with prose, I invariably lifted the piece of cardboard which I employed to shelter my boarders and enquired into the happenings of the night. These daily inspections were not so feasible in the large glass cage, whose numerous dwellings would all be thrown into confusion, if they were to be examined one by one and then methodically set in order as discovered. With my pots of Black Scorpions, the inspection was the matter of a moment.

It was well for me that I always had this auxiliary establishment before my eyes. On the 22nd of July, at six o'clock in the morning, raising the cardboard screen, I found a mother beneath it, with her little ones clustering on her back like a sort of white cloak. I experienced one of those moments of sweet contentment which, at intervals, reward the long-suffering observer. For the first time I had before my eyes the fine spectacle of the Scorpioness clad in her young. The delivery was quite recent: it must have taken place during the night, for, on the previous evening, the mother was naked.

Further successes awaited me: on the next day, a second mother is whitened with her brood: the day after that, two others at a time are in the same condition. That makes four. It is more than my ambition hoped for. With four families of Scorpions and a few quiet days before me, we may find some pleasure in life.

All the more so as fortune loads me with her favours. Ever since the first discovery in the jars, I have been thinking of the glass jars and asking myself whether the Languedocian Scorpion might not be as forward as her black sister. Let us make haste and see.

I turn over the twenty-five tiles. A glorious success! I feel one of those hot waves of enthusiasm with which I was familiar at the age of twenty rush through my old veins. Under three out of the total number of tiles, I find a mother laden with her family. One has young that are already quite of a fair size, about a week old, as my subsequent observations informed me; the two others have borne their children recently, during the recent night, as is proved by certain remnants jealously guarded under the paunch. We shall see presently what these remnants represent.

July runs to an end, August and September pass and nothing more occurs to swell my collection. The period of the family, therefore, for both Scorpions is the second fortnight in July. From that time onwards everything is finished. And yet, among my guests in the black cage, there are still some females as big and fat as those from whom I have obtained progeny. I reckoned on these too for an increase in the population; all the appearances authorized me to do so. Winter comes and none of them has answered my expectations. The business, which seemed close at hand, has been put off to next year: a fresh proof of long gestation, very singular in the case of an animal of a lower order.

I transfer each mother and her product, separately, into medium-sized receptacles, which facilitate conscientious observation. At the early hour of my visit, those brought to bed during the night have still a part of the brood sheltered under their bellies. Pushing the mother aside with a straw, I discover, amid the heap of young not yet hoisted on the maternal back, objects that utterly upset all that the books have taught me on this subject. The Scorpions, they say are viviparous. The scientific expression lacks exactitude: the young do not first see the light in the shape with which we are familiar.

And this must be so. How would you have the outstretched claws, the sprawling legs, the curled-up tails make their way through the maternal passages? The cumberous little animal could never pass through the narrow outlets. It must needs enter the world packed up and sparing of space.

The remnants found under the mothers, in fact, show me eggs, real eggs, similar, or very nearly, to those which dissection extracts from the ovaries at an advanced stage of pregnancy. The little animal, economically compressed to the dimensions of a grain of rice, has its tail laid along its belly, its claws flattened against its chest, its legs pressed to its sides, so that the small easily gliding oval mass presents not the slightest protuberance. On the forehead, dots of an intense black mark the eyes. The tiny insect floats in a drop of transparent moisture, which is for the moment its world, its atmosphere, contained by a pellicle of exquisite delicacy.

These objects are really eggs. There were thirty or forty of them, at first, in the Languedocian Scorpion's litter; not quite so many in the Black Scorpion's. Intervening too late in the nocturnal confinement, I am present at the finish. The little that remains, however, is sufficient to convince me. The Scorpion is in reality oviparous; only, her eggs hatch very speedily and the liberation of the young follows very soon after the laying.

Now how does this liberation take place? I enjoy the remarkable privilege of witnessing it. I see the mother with the points of her mandibles delicately seizing, tearing, peeling off and lastly swallowing the membrane of the egg. She strips her new-born offspring with the fastidious care and fondness of the Sheep and the Cat eating the fœtal wrappers. Not a scratch on that scarce formed flesh, not a limb strained, in spite of the clumsiness of the tool employed.

I cannot get over my surprise: the Scorpion has initiated the race into processes of maternity bordering on our own. In the distant days of the carboniferous periods, when the first Scorpion appeared, the tender cases of child-birth were already preparing. The egg, the equivalent of the long-sleeping seed, the egg, as already possessed by the reptile and the fish and later to be possessed by the bird and almost the whole body of insects, was the contemporary of an infinitely more delicate organism which ushered in the viviparousness of the higher animals. The incubation of the germ did not take place outside, amidst the threatening conflict of things; it was accomplished in the mother's womb.

The progressive movements of life know no gradual stages, from fair to good, from good to excellent; they proceed by leaps and bounds, in some cases advancing, in some recoiling. The ocean has its rythmical ebb and flow. Life, that other ocean, more unfathomable than the watery ocean, has its ebb and flow likewise. Will it have any other tides? Who can say it will? Who can say that it will not?

If the Sheep did not assist by swallowing the membranous envelopes after picking them up with her lips, never would the Lamb succeed in extricating itself from its swaddling-clothes. In the same way, the little Scorpion calls for its mother's aid. I see some that, caught in stickiness, writhe aimlessly in the half-torn ovarian sac, unable to free themselves. It wants a touch of the mother's teeth to complete the deliverance. It is doubtful even whether the young insect contributes to effect the laceration. Its weakness is of no avail against that other weakness, the natal envelope, though this be as slender as the inner lining of an onion-skin.

The young Chick has a temporary callosity at the end of its beak, which serves it as a pick-axe to break the shell. The young Scorpion, condensed, to economise space, to the dimensions of a grain of rice, waits inertly for help from without. The mother has to do everything. She works with such a will that the accessories of childbirth disappear altogether, even the few sterile eggs being swept away with the others in the general flow. Not a remnant of the now useless tatters; everything has returned to the mother's stomach; and the spot of ground that received the litter is swept absolutely clear.

So here we have the young scrupulously cleaned and free. They are white. Their length from head to tail, measures nine millimetres3 in the Languedocian Scorpion and four4 in the Black. As the liberating toilet is completed, they climb, first one and then the other, on the mother's back, hoisting themselves, without excessive haste, along the claws, which the Scorpion holds flat on the ground, in order to facilitate the ascent. Close packed one against the other, entangled at random, they form a continuous sheet upon her back. With the aid of their little claws, they settle themselves pretty firmly. I find some difficulty in sweeping them away with the point of a camel-hair pencil without more or less hurting the feeble creatures. At this stage neither steed nor burden budges: it is the fit moment for experiment. Clad in her offspring assembled to form a mantle of white muslin, the Scorpion is a spectacle worthy of attention. She remains motionless, with her tail curled on high. If I threaten the family too closely with a straw, she at once lifts her two claws in an angry attitude, rarely adopted in her own defence. The two fists are raised as if for sparring, the nippers wide open, ready to thrust and parry. The tail is seldom brandished: to loosen it suddenly would give a shock to the spine and perhaps make a part of the load fall to the ground. The bold, sudden, imposing menace of the fists suffices.

My curiosity takes no notice of it. I push off one of the little ones and place it facing its mother, a finger's breadth distant. The mother does not seem to trouble about the accident: motionless she was, motionless she remains. Why perturb herself about a tumble? The fallen child will be quite able to manage for itself. It gesticulates, it moves about: and then, finding one of the mother's claws within its reach, it clambers up nimbly enough and joins the crowd of its brothers. It resumes its seat in the saddle, but is far from displaying the agility of the Lycosa's sons, who are expert riders, versed in the art of vaulting on horseback.

The experiment is repeated on a larger scale. This time, I sweep a part of the load to the ground; the little ones are scattered to no very great distance. There is a somewhat lengthy, hesitating pause. While the brats wander about, without quite knowing where to go, the mother at last becomes at the state of affairs. With her two arms—I am speaking of the pedipalpi that carry the pincers—with her two arms joined in a semicircle, she rakes and gathers the sand so as to bring the truants towards her. This is done awkwardly, clumsily, with no precautions against accidental crushing. The Hen, with a soft, clucking call, makes the wandering Chicks return to the pale; the Scorpion collects her family with the sweep of the rake. All are safe and sound nevertheless. As soon as they come in contact with the mother, they climb up and form themselves again into the dorsal group.

Strangers are admitted to this group as well as the legitimate offspring. If, with the camel-hair broom, I dislodge a matron's family, wholly or in part, and place it within reach of a second mother, laden with her own family, the latter will collect the young ones by armfuls, as she would her own offspring, and meekly allow the newcomers to mount upon her back. One would say that she adopts them, were the expression not too ambitious. There is no adoption. We have once more the blindness of the Lycosa, who is incapable of distinguishing between her own and another's progeny, and welcomes all that swarms about her legs.

I expected to come upon excursions similar to those of the Lycosa, whom it is not unusual to meet scouring the heath with her pack of children on her back. The Scorpion knows nothing of these diversions. Once she becomes a mother, for sometime she does not leave her home, not even in the evening, at the hour when others sally forth to frolic. Barricaded in her cell, not troubling to eat, she watches over the upbringing of her young.

As a matter of fact, these frail creatures have a ticklish ordeal to undergo: they have, one might say, to be born a second time. They prepare for it by immobility and by an inward labour not unlike that which turns the larva into the perfect insect. In spite of their fairly correct appearance as Scorpions, the young ones have rather indistinct features, which look as though seen through a mist. One is inclined to credit them with a sort of child's smock, which they must throw off in order to grow slender and acquire a definite outline.

A week spent without moving, on the mother's back, is required for this work. Then there takes place an excoriation which I hesitate to describe by the expression moult, so greatly does it differ from the true moult, undergone later at repeated intervals. For the latter, the skin splits over the thorax; and the animal emerges through this single fissure, leaving a dry, cast-off garment behind it, similar in shape to the Scorpion that has just discarded it. The empty mould retains the exact outline of the moulded animal.

But, this time, we have something different. I place a few young ones in the act of shedding their skin on a sheet of glass. They are motionless, sorely tried, it seems, almost spent. The skin bursts, without special lines of cleavage; it tears at one and the same time in front, behind, at the sides; the legs come out of their gaiters, the claws leave their gauntlets, the tail quits its scabbard. The cast skin falls in rags on all sides at once. It is a peeling without order and in tatters. When it is done, the stripped insects present the normal appearance of Scorpions. They have also acquired agility. Although still pale in tint, they are nimble, quick to set foot to earth in order to run and play beside their mother. The most striking part of this progress is the rapid growth. The young of the Languedocian Scorpion measured nine millimetres in length; they now measure fourteen.5 Those of the Black Scorpion have grown from four to six or seven millimetres.6 The length increases by one half, which nearly trebles the volume.

Surprised by this sudden growth, we wonder what the cause can be, for the little ones have taken no food. Their weight has not increased; on the contrary, it has diminished; for we must remember that the skin has been cast. The volume increases, but not the mass. There is, therefore, a distension up to a certain point, which may be compared with that of inorganic bodies under the influence of heat. A secret change takes place, which groups the living molecules into a more spacious combination; and the volume increases without the addition of fresh materials. One who, possessed of a fine patience and suitably equipped, cared to follow the rapid changes of this architecture would, I think, reap a harvest of some value. I, in my penury, abandon the problem to others.

The remnants of the peeling process are white strips, satiny rags, which, so far from falling to the ground, adhere to the back of the mother Scorpion, especially near the base of the legs, where they become tangled into a soft carpet on which the lately-stripped insects rest. The mount now boasts a saddle-cloth well adapted to hold her restless riders in their seats. Whether these have to alight or to remount, the layer of tatters, now become a solid harness, affords support for rapid movement.

When I topple over the family with a slight stroke of the camel-hair pencil, it is amusing to see how quickly the unhorsed ones resume their seat in the saddle. The fringes of the housings are grasped, the tail is used as a lever and, with a bound, the rider is in his place. This curious carpet, a real boarding-net which makes climbing easy, lasts, without dislocations, for nearly a week, that is to say, until the emancipation. Then it falls off of its own accord, either as a whole or piecemeal, and nothing remains of it when the young are dispersed over the surrounding country.

Meantime, signs of the colouring appear; the tail and belly are tinged with saffron, the claws assume the soft brilliancy of translucent amber. Youth beautifies all things. The little Languedocian Scorpions are really magnificent. If they remained thus, if they did not carry a poison-still, soon to become threatening, they would be pretty creatures which we should find a pleasure in rearing. Soon the wish for emancipation awakens in them. They gladly descend from the mother's back to frolic merrily round about her. If they stray too far, the mother cautions them and brings them back again by sweeping the rake of her arms over the sand.

At the time of the siesta, the sight furnished by the Scorpioness is almost as good as that of the Hen and her Chicks at rest. Most of the little ones are on the ground, pressed close against their mother: a few are stationed on the white saddle-cloth, a delightful cushion. There are some who clamber up the the mother's tail, perch on the crest of the curve and seem to delight in looking down from this point of vantage upon the crowd. More acrobats arrive, who dislodge them and take their places. All want their share in the curiosities provided by the conning-tower.

The bulk of the family is around the mother; there is a constant swarm of brats that crawl under the belly and there squat, leaving their forehead, with the gleaming black eye-points, outside. The more restless prefer the mother's legs, which to them represent a gymnasium; they here swing as on a trapeze. Next, at their leisure, the whole troop climb up to her back again, resume their places and settle down; and nothing more stirs, neither mother nor little ones.

This period, during which the Scorpion is matured and prepared for emancipation, lasts a week, exactly as long as the strange process that trebles the volume without food. The family remains upon the mother's back for a fortnight, all told. The Lycosa carries her young for six or seven months, during which time they are always active and lively, although unfed. What do those of the Scorpion eat, at least after the excoriation that has given them agility and a new life? Does the mother invite them to her meals and reserve the tenderest morsels of her repasts for them? She invites nobody; she reserves nothing.

I serve her a Locust, chosen among the small game that seems to me best-suited to the delicate nature of her offspring. While she gnaws the morsel, without troubling in the least about her surroundings, one of the little ones slips down her back, advances over her head and leans down to enquire what is happening. He touches her jaws with the tip of his leg; then briskly he decamps, startled. He makes off; and he is well-advised. The abyss engaged in the work of mastication, so far from reserving him a mouthful, might perhaps snap him up and swallow him without giving him a further thought.

A second is hanging on behind the Locust, the fore part of whose body the mother is munching. He nibbles, he pulls, eager for a bit. His perseverance comes to nothing: the fare is too tough.

It is plain enough to see: the appetite is awakening; the young would gladly accept food, if the mother took the least care to offer them any, especially food adapted to the frailty of their tender stomachs: but she just eats for herself and that is all.

What do you want, O my pretty little Scorpions, who have provided me with such delightful moments? You want to go away, to some distant place, in search of victuals, of the tiniest of tiny beasties. I can see it by your restless roving. You run away from your mother, who, on her side, ceases to know you. You are strong enough: the hour has come to disperse.

If I knew exactly what infinitesimal game is to your liking and if I had sufficient time to procure it for you, I should love to continue your upbringing, but not among the potsherds of your native cage, in the company of your elders. I know their intolerant spirit. The ogres would eat you up, my children. Your own mothers would not spare you. You are strangers to them henceforth. Next year, at the wedding-season, they would eat you, the jealous creatures! You had better go; prudence demands it.

Where could I lodge you and how could I feed you? The best thing is to say good-bye, not without a certain regret on my part. One of these days, I will take you and scatter you in your own domain, the rock-strewn slope where the sun is so hot. There you will find brothers and sisters who, hardly larger than yourselves, are already leading solitary lives under their little stones, sometimes no bigger than a thumb-nail. There you will learn the hard struggle for life better than you would with me.

1 Louis Pasteur (1822–1895), the famous French chemist and bacteriologist.—*Translator's Note.*

2 Léon Dufour (1780–1865) was an army-surgeon who served with distinction in several campaigns and subsequently practised as a Doctor in the Landes. He attained great eminence as a naturalist. Cf. *The Life of the Spider*: chap. i.—*Translator's Note.*

3 .35 inch.—*Translator's Note.*

4 .15 inch.—*Translator's Note.*

5 .351 increased to .546 inch.—*Translator's Note.*

6 .156 increased to .235 or .275 inch.—*Translator's Note.*

SOME PLANT LICE

CHAPTER I
THE PENTATOMÆ AND THEIR EGGS

Of the forms which life is able to bestow on her creations, that of the bird's egg is one of the simplest and loveliest. Nowhere do we find the beauty of the circle and the ellipse, the geometrical bases of organic bodies, combined with greater precision. At one of the poles is the sphere, the perfect form, capable of enclosing the greatest volume in the smallest envelope; at the other is the point of the ellipsoid, which tempers the monotonous austerities of the big end.

The colour-scheme, likewise very simple, adds its graces to those of form. Some eggs display the dull white of chalk, others the translucid white of polished ivory. The Wheat-ear's are a delicate blue, like that of a sky freshly washed by a rain-storm; the Nightingale's are a dark green, like that of a pickled olive; the eggs of certain Warblers are tinted with an exquisite carnation, like that of roses still in the bud.

The Yellow-hammer scrawls an indecipherable scribble on her eggs; that is to say, the shells display mottled markings, an artistic mixture of lines and blots. The Butcher-birds encircle the large end with a speckled crown; the Blackbird and the Raven sprinkle brown splashes, innocent of design, on a greenish-blue ground; the Curlew and the Gull employ large spots like those on the Leopard's coat; and so with the rest; each has its speciality, its trade-mark, always designed in sober colours, the mere matching of which constitutes a merit.

With the exquisite simplicity of its geometry and its ornament, the bird's egg enchants the least cultivated eye. In return for the little services which they render me, I sometimes admit to my study certain small boys of the neighbourhood, zealous searchers all. Now what do these simple-minded youngsters see in my work-room, of which they have heard all sorts of wonders? They see big, glass-fronted cupboards in which a thousand curious things are arranged, the cumbersome accumulations that gather about any one who investigates stones, plants and animals. Shells predominate.

Huddling together in mutual encouragement, my shy visitors admire the magnificent Sea-snails of every shape and colour; they point a finger at this or that shell which, by the lustre of its mother-of-pearl, its size and its strange protuberances, is especially conspicuous in the midst of all the rest. They gaze at my treasures and I watch their faces. I read on them surprise, amazement and nothing more.

These things out of the sea, too complex in formation to impress a novice, are mysterious objects that speak no known language. My little giddy-pates are bewildered by these corkscrew stair-cases, these scrolls and spirals and conchs, whose geometry is beyond their comprehension. They are left almost cold before this display of oceanic wealth. If I could get at what lies at the back of their minds, these children would say:

"How funny!"

They would never say:

"How pretty!"

It is quite another story with the boxes in which the birds'-eggs of the district are arranged, clutch by clutch, lying on cotton-wool, protected from the light. Now their cheeks flush with excitement and they whisper, in one another's ears, which they would choose of the finest group in the box. There is no amazement now, but ingenuous admiration. It is true that the egg recalls the nest and the young birds, those incomparable joys of childhood. Nevertheless, a rush of reverent emotion evoked by the beautiful may be read on their faces. The gems of the sea astound my little visitors; the simple beauty of the eggs arouses a more human ecstasy.

In the very great majority of cases, the insect's egg is far from attaining this consummate perfection, which impresses even the unaccustomed gaze. The usual shapes are the sphere, the spindle or cone, and the cylinder, with rounded ends, none of which is especially graceful, owing to the absence of harmonious combinations of curves. Many of them are dingy in colour; some, by their excessive richness, form a violent contrast with the shortcomings of the germ inside. The eggs of certain Moths and Butterflies are beads of bronze or nickel. In these life seems to germinate within the rigid walls of a metal box.

If we employ the magnifying-glass, we find that ornamentation of detail is not unusual, but it is always complicated, without that nobler simplicity which constitutes true beauty. The Clythræ1 enclose their eggs in a shell whose substance is laminated in scales like those of a hop-cone, or twisted into intersecting diagonal fillets; certain Locusts engrave their spindles, scooping out spiral rows of little pits like those of a thimble. There is, to be sure, no lack of prettiness in all this, but how far removed is such exuberance from the noble austerity of beauty!

The insect has ovarian æsthetics of its own, which have no relation to those of the bird. I know of one case, however, in which comparison is possible. An insect of indifferent repute, a woodland Bug, the Pentatoma of the naturalists, may offer its egg for comparison with the bird's. This flat-bodied insect, emitting a horrible smell, lays masterpieces of elegant simplicity, and, at the same time, of mechanical ingenuity; it disgusts us by its cosmetic, its hair-oil; but it interests us by its egg, which is worthy to rank beside that of the bird.

I have just made a discovery on a sprig of asparagus. It is a cluster of eggs, about thirty in number, arranged in rows, in close contact, like the beads on a piece of embroidery. I recognize the eggs of a woodland Bug. The hatching took place some little time ago, for the family has not yet dispersed. The empty eggshells have remained in place without any loss of shape, except that their lids are open.

What a delightful collection of miniature vases in translucent alabaster, barely clouded with light grey! One would like to read a fairy-tale of the world of tiny things in which the fairies take tea out of such cups as these. The body of the vessel, a graceful oval cut square at the top, shows a delicate brown network of polygonal meshes. Imagine the top of a bird's egg neatly removed, making a dainty little goblet of the remainder, and you have something very like the egg of the Bug. In either case there are the same gentle curves.

Here the resemblance ceases. It is in the upper part of the egg that the insect displays its originality; its creation is a box with a lid. This slightly convex cover is ornamented, like the body of the jar, with a network of fine mesh; it is further embellished along the edge with an opal border. At the hatching it swings open as on a hinge and comes away all of a piece. Sometimes it falls off and leaves the jar wide open; sometimes it falls back into its normal position, once more closing the jar, which looks as though it were still intact. Lastly, the mouth is surrounded by very fine, thread-like attachments. These are, as it were, rivets to hold the lid in position, so as to close the vase hermetically.

We must not overlook one exceedingly characteristic detail. Quite close to the rim, inside the shell, there is always visible, after the hatching, a mark like a broad arrow, or a capital T, with the arms deflected like those of an anchor. What is the meaning of this infinitesimal detail? Is it a latch, a sort of lock with a bolt and hasp? Is it a potter's mark, conferring a certificate of origin on the masterpiece? What a strange effort of ceramic art merely to hold the egg of a Bug!

The young ones have not yet left the battery of jars from which they recently emerged. Gathered together in a heap, they are waiting for the bath of air and sunlight to harden them before dispersing and implanting their suckers where they please. They are plump, thickset, black, with the under surface of the belly red and the sides laced with the same colour. How did they get out of their jars? By what artifice did they raise the firmly-sealed lid? Let us try to find the answer to this interesting question.

It is the end of April. In the enclosure, just outside my door, the camphor-scented rosemaries are in full flower, bringing me visits from a multitude of insects which I can consult at any time. Various species of Pentatomæ abound, but do not lend themselves to precise observation, by reason of their wandering life. If I want to know exactly which egg belongs to which species or, above all, if I want to learn how the hatching is accomplished, it will not be enough to rely upon chance inspections of the flowering shrubs. It will be better to resort to rearing the insects under a wire-gauze cover.

My captives, isolated according to species and represented each by a certain number of couples, give me hardly any trouble. All they need is a cheerful sun and a bunch of rosemary daily renewed. I add to the furnishing of the cage a few leafy twigs from various bushes. The insect will choose whichever suits her as the spot for laying her eggs.

By the first fortnight in May the imprisoned Bugs have provided me with eggs in excess of my hopes, eggs at once collected, together with their support, species by species, and placed in small glass tubes, where, unless I fail in vigilance, I shall easily be able to follow the delicate hatching-process.

It is really a beautiful, a most delightful collection, and would be quite worthy to figure beside the eggs of the bird, if larger dimensions came to the assistance of our feeble sight. From the moment we have to resort to the microscope, we allow the splendid to escape us. Let us magnify the Bug's egg under the lens and it will amaze us as surely as the Stonechat's sky-blue egg, and perhaps even more. What a pity that such beauty escapes our admiration by its minuteness!

The shape is never a complete ovoid: that is the bird's perquisite. The upper end of the Pentatoma's egg is always finished off with a sudden truncation, into which a slightly convex lid is fitted, and we have before us a tiny ciborium, a delicious casket, an antique urn, a cylindrical cask with rounded ends, a full-bodied vase of Oriental porcelain, with ornaments consisting of bands, rosettes or traceries, varying according to the mother's individual taste. Always, moreover, when the egg is empty, we find a most delicate fringe of herring-boned threads running round the mouth.

These are the rivets to fasten the lid, which are pushed up and back at the moment when the new-born insect is released.

Lastly, in all these egg-shells, after the hatching, we find inside them, quite close to the rim, that black mark in the shape of a broad arrow, of which we have already asked ourselves whether it is a trade-mark or a sort of lock or bolt. The future will show us how far our guesses fall short of the reality.

The eggs are never sown at random. The whole batch is laid in a close-packed group, in regular ranks of varying lengths, so that they make a sort of mosaic of beads firmly fixed to their common support, usually a leaf. They adhere so firmly that we may brush the leaf with a camel-hair pencil, or even touch them with the finger, without in any way disturbing their beautiful arrangement. After the young have gone we find the open shells still in position, like so many little jam-pots standing in rows on a market-woman's barrow.

Let me end by giving a few specific details. The eggs of the Black-horned Pentatoma (*P. nigricorne*) are cylindroid in form, the base being a segment of a sphere. The lid, bearing a broad white band at the edge, frequently, but not always, has in the centre a transparent protuberance, a sort of knob like that on the lid of a preserve-jar. Its entire surface is smooth and glossy, with no other ornament than its simplicity. The colour varies according to the degree of maturity. When recently laid the eggs are of a uniform straw-yellow: later, owing to the gradual organization of the germ, they turn a pale orange, with a triangular bright-red patch in the centre of the lid. When empty they are a magnificent, pellucid opal-white, except the lid, which has become transparent as glass.

Of the clutches of eggs obtained the most numerous was a patch of nine rows, each containing about a dozen eggs. The total was thus about a hundred. But usually the number of eggs is smaller than this, amounting to only half as many or less. Groups containing about a score of eggs are not uncommon. The enormous difference between these extremes testifies to multiple layings at different spots, which, in view of the insect's rapid flight, may be at quite a distance from one another. This detail will be of value when the time comes.

The Pale-Green Pentatoma (*P. praesinum*) moulds her eggs in little barrels, ovoid at the bottom and adorned over their whole surface with a network of fine polygonal meshes in relief. Their colour is a sooty brown, and, after the hatching, a very light brown. The largest groups of eggs contain thirty or so. It is probably to this species that the eggs belong which first attracted my attention on a sprig of asparagus.

As for the Berry Pentatoma (*P. baccarum*) here we again have barrels with rounded ends, covered all over the surface with a tracery of meshes. At first they are opaque and dark; then, being empty, they become translucent and white or pale-pink. Of these eggs I find groups of fifty and others of fifteen or even less.

That blessed plant of the kitchen-gardens, the cabbage, gives me the Ornate Pentatoma (*P. ornatum*), striped black and red. The eggs of this species are the prettiest of all in colouring. They are like little casks with the two ends convex, especially the lower. The microscope shows us a surface engraved with pits, like those of a thimble, arranged with exquisite regularity. At the top and bottom of the cylinder there is a broad dull-black band; on the sides is a wide white belt with four large black spots symmetrically placed. The lid, surrounded with snow-white filaments and edged with white, swells into a black dome with a central white spot. In short, a funeral urn, with its violent contrast of coal-black and creamy white. The Etruscans would have considered it a magnificent model for their burial vessels.

These eggs, with their funeral ornamentation, are arranged in small groups, generally in two rows. There are hardly a dozen all told: a fresh proof that the eggs must be laid in a number of batches and at different points; for the Cabbage Bug cannot limit herself to this paltry number when one of her relatives exceeds the hundred.

May is not over before the various batches of eggs collected and placed in tubes hatch out, first one and then another. Two or three weeks are enough to develop the germ. This is the time for constant vigilance, if I wish to understand the mechanism employed for the emergence and, above all, the function of the strange tool, with the three black arms, which I find in every shell, at the edge of the opening, once the new-born larva has departed.

Those eggs which are translucent from the outset—for example, those of the Black-horned Pentatoma—enable me, in the first place, to discover that the implement of unknown use makes its appearance rather late, when the approaching deliverance is announced by a change in the colour of the lid. It is not, therefore, an original part of the egg, as this descended from the ovaries; it is elaborated during the process of development, and even at a somewhat advanced phase, when the little Bug has already been formed.

We must therefore cease to regard it, as I did at first, as a spring, a lock, some sort of a hinge to hold the lid in place. An actual device for keeping the egg closed and protecting the germ would have to be in existence when the egg was laid. And it is just at the end, when the time has come to leave it, that the egg reveals this device. It is a question no longer of closing, but of opening. And, in this case, might not the puzzling implement be a key, a lever to force open the lid, held on by thread-like rivets, and perhaps also by the glue of an adhesive? Assiduous patience will tell us.

Holding the magnifying-glass above my test-tubes, which I examine every moment, at last I witness the hatching. The process is just beginning. The lid is rising imperceptibly at one pole of its diameter; at the other it is tilting like a door on its hinges. The youngster has its back to the wall of the barrel, just below the edge of the lid, which is already gaping, a capital situation, enabling me to follow with some exactness the progress of the deliverance.

The little Bug, shrunken and motionless, has its head crowned with a skin cap, suspected rather than seen, so fine is it. Later, when it falls off, this cap will be plainly visible. It serves as the base of a trihedral angle. The three arms forming this angle are rigid and intensely black and look as if they ought to be of a horny nature. Two of them extend between the eyes, which are bright red; the third passes down behind the head and is connected with the others, right and left, by a dark, very fine line. I might very well regard these dark lines as tense threads, ligaments which brace the three arms of the apparatus and prevent them from slipping farther apart, thereby blunting the point of the angle, which is itself the key of the casket, that is, the rammer for pushing back the lid. This three-cornered mitre protects the head, which is still soft and fleshy and incapable of forcing the obstruction: with its adamantine point truly applied right at the edge of the lid it has a firm grip of the disk which has to be unfastened.

This mechanism, this cap surmounted by an armoured point, must have its motive force. Where is it? It is at the top of the head. Look carefully, and there, involving a certain small area, almost a point, you will see rapid pulsations, we might almost say piston strokes, produced, beyond a doubt, by sudden waves of blood. By hurriedly injecting what little fluid its body contains under its pliant cranium, the tiny creature turns its weakness into energy. The three-cornered helmet rises, pushing upwards, always pressing its point firmly on the same point of the lid. No blow is struck upon the tool; there is no intermittent percussion, but a continuous thrust.

The operation is so laborious that it lasts for more than an hour. By imperceptible degrees the lid is unfastened and rises obliquely, but as a rule continues to adhere to the rim of the vase at the opposite pole of the diameter. At this pivotal point, where it would seem that there must be a hinge, the lens reveals nothing peculiar. Here, as every elsewhere, there is a mere row of threads, drawn down to form rivets for closing the cask. On the side opposite the point attacked, these rivets, less disturbed than the rest, do not quite give way, act as a hinge.

Little by little the tiny creature emerges from its shell. The legs and antennæ, economically folded over the thorax and abdomen, are completely motionless. Nothing moves, yet the Bug protrudes farther and farther from its casket, doubtless with the aid of a process like that employed by the larva of the Balaninus,2 on leaving its nut. The flow of blood which causes the piston-strokes of the cranium distends also that part of the body which is already free and converts it into a supporting cushion; the hinder part, which is still imprisoned, is diminished accordingly and in its turn enters the narrow opening. The insect passes through a draw-plate, so gently and carefully that the most I can detect is a tentative rocking to and fro at distant intervals as it drags itself from its socket.

At last the rivets are forced, the casket is open, and the lid, now on a slant, is sufficiently raised. The three-cornered mitre has done its work. What will become of it? Henceforth useless as a tool, it has to disappear; and, as a matter of fact, I see it discarded. The filmy head-dress which served as its foundation tears, becomes a tattered rag and very slowly slips over the Bug's ventral surface, dragging with it the hard little black contrivance, which still retains its shape. Scarcely has this relic slipped midway down the belly when the tiny creature, hitherto motionless in the attitude of a mummy, frees its legs and antennæ from their economical position, stretches them out and impatiently waves them to and fro. It is over: the insect leaves its sheath.

The instrument of release, still in the shape of a T with arms bent slightly downwards and sideways, remains sticking to the wall of the shell, near the opening. Long after the insect's departure the lens finds the ingenious triangle in its place. Its formation is the same in the various Pentatomæ; but until we surprise the insect in the act of hatching its function is incomprehensible.

A word more on the manner of opening the lidded casket. I have said that the young Bug has its back to the wall of the little barrel, as far as possible from the centre. It is here that it is born, dons its tiara and afterwards pushes with its head. Why does it not occupy the central region, a position which would seem to be prescribed by the shape of the egg and the more effectual protection of the grub's early frailty? Can there be any advantage in being born elsewhere, on the very circumference?

Yes, there is, and a very distinct advantage, of a mechanical order. With the top of its head, which throbs with the rushes of blood, the new-born insect thrusts his pointed cap against the lid to be unfastened. What can be the cranial thrust of a drop of albumen but lately congealed into a living entity? He would be a bold man who should venture to reply, so far is it beneath all evaluation. And this mere nothing has to push open the solid lid of the box.

Let us picture the thrust applied to the centre. In that case the effort to dislodge the lid, the veriest trifle of an effort, would be uniformly distributed over the entire circumference, and all the rivets which fasten it would play their part in the resistance offered. Singly, the stitches would give way before the tiny force available; but all together they are invincible. The method of the central thrust is therefore impracticable.

If we wished to loosen a nailed plank, it would be an illogical action to bang it in the middle. The whole of the nails would react in a common and insurmountable resistance. On the contrary, we attack it at one end; we apply the leverage of our implement progressively to one nail after another. The little Bug in its casket does much the same: it pushes out the extreme edge of the lid, so that, beginning at the point attacked, the rivets give way, one by one. The total resistance is overcome because it is divided.

Well done, little Bug! You have your own science of mechanics, based on the same laws as ours; you know the secrets of the lever and the lifting-jack. To break its shell, the nascent bird grows a callosity on its beak, a pick-axe point whose function is to break down the chalky wall piecemeal. When the task is accomplished this callus, the tool of a day, disappears. You have something better than the bird's device.

When the hour of your emergence comes, you don a cap in which three stiff ribs converge to a point. At the base of this appliance your soft cranium acts like the piston of an hydraulic press. Thus attacked, the roof of your hut is unfastened and thrown back. The bird's callosity disappears when the shell is in pieces; so does the mitre with which you push out the head of your barrel. As soon as the lid opens wide enough to let you pass, you doff your cap with its tripod of rods.

Your egg, however, is not broken; there is no violent demolition such as that practised by the bird. When empty, the egg-shell is not a ruin; it is still the graceful little egg that it was in the beginning, rendered yet more exquisite by its translucence, which enhances its beauties. In what school, little Bug, did you learn the art of opening your natal casket and the use of your little contrivance? There are those who will say:

"In the school of chance."

But you, in all humility, cock your mitre and reply:

"That's not true."

The Pentatoma is noted for another detail, which, if it were definitely proved, would surpass a hundredfold the marvels of the egg. I quote the following passage from De Geer,3 the Swedish Réaumur4:

"The Bugs of this species (*Pentatoma griseum*) live on the birch-tree. In the early part of July, I found several of them accompanied by their young. Each mother was surrounded by a troop of young ones, to the number of twenty, thirty and even forty. She always kept close beside them, commonly on one of the catkins of the tree that contained her eggs, and sometimes on a leaf. I have noted that these little Bugs and their mother do not always remain on the same spot, and that as soon as the mother begins to move away all her little ones follow her, stopping whenever the mother calls a halt. She thus leads them from catkin to catkin or leaf to leaf and takes them wherever she pleases, as a Hen does her Chicks.

"There are Bugs that do not leave their offspring; they even keep watch over them and take the greatest care of them while they are young. One day I happened to cut a young birch-branch peopled with such a family and I first observed the extremely uneasy mother, incessantly beating her wings with a rapid movement, without, however, stirring from the spot, as though to drive away the enemy that had just approached, whereas, in any other circumstances, she would at once have flown away or sought to escape, which proves that she was remaining only to defend her young."

M. Karl de Geer has observed that it is chiefly against the male of her species that the mother Bug is obliged to defend her young, because he tries to devour them wherever he comes upon them; and on such occasions she always tries with all her might to protect them against his attacks.

In his *Curiosités d'historie naturelle*, Boitard still farther embellishes the picture of family life painted by De Geer:

"It is most curious," he says, "to see how the mother Bug, when a few drops of rain are falling, leads her young under a leaf or the fork of a branch to shelter them. Even there her anxious affection is not reassured; she drives them into a closely-packed flock, places herself in their midst and covers them with her wings, which she spreads over them umbrella-wise; and, in spite of the discomfort of her position, she retains this attitude of a brooding Hen until the storm has blown over."

Shall I confess it? This umbrella made of the mother's wings during showery weather, this procession of a Hen leading her Chicks, this devotion in warding off the attacks of a father inclined to devour his family leave me just a little incredulous, without surprising me, experience having taught me that the books are full of little anecdotes incapable of surviving the ordeal of a strict investigation.

An incomplete observation, wrongly interpreted, sets the story going. Then come the compilers, who faithfully hand down the legend, the unsound fruit of the imagination; and error, confirmed by repetition, becomes an article of faith. What, for example, was not reported of the Sacred Beetle and her pill, the Necrophorus5 and her work of burial, the Hunting Wasp and her game, the Cicada and her well, before the truth was arrived at? The real, which is perfectly simple, and supremely beautiful, too often escapes us, giving way before the imaginary, which is less troublesome to acquire. Instead of going back to the facts and seeing for ourselves, we blindly follow tradition. To-day no one would write a few lines on the Pentatomæ without dragging in the Swedish naturalist's doubtful story, and no one, as far as I know, has mentioned the genuine marvels connected with the mechanism of the hatching.

What can De Geer have seen? The observer's high standing gives us confidence; none the less, I shall take the liberty of experimenting in my turn before accepting the master's statements.

The Grey Bug, the subject of my story, is less frequent than the others in my neighbourhood: on the rosemaries in the enclosure, my field of exploration, I find three or four which, when placed under glass, do not give me any eggs. The set-back does not seem irreparable: what the grey refuses to reveal the green or the yellow or the red-and-black striped—one and all of similar formation and like habits—will show me. In species so closely akin, the family cares of the one must, in all but a few details, be reproduced in the others. Let us then note how the four Pentatomæ reared in captivity behave in the matter of their new-born young. Their unanimous testimony will convince us.

At the very outset I was struck by a fact which disagreed with what I had a right to expect in a future Hen leading her Chicks. The mother pays no attention to her eggs. When the last has been laid in its place at the extreme end of the last row, she makes off, heedless of what she has left behind her. She does not trouble about it any more, does not return to it. If the hazards of her wanderings lead her up to it, she steps on the heap, crosses it and passes on, indifferent. The evidence leaves nothing to be desired: the coming upon a patch of eggs is an incident of no interest to the mother.

We must not attribute this negligence to the aberrations which may possibly occur in a state of captivity. In the perfect liberty of the fields I have come across many batches of eggs, perhaps including those of the Grey Bug; never have I seen the mother standing by her eggs, which she would have to do if her family required protection as soon as hatched.

The gravid mother is a quick flier and of a vagabond temperament. Once she has flown to a considerable distance from the leaf which has received her eggs, how is she to remember, two or three weeks later, that the hour for hatching is at hand? How is she to find her eggs again? Moreover, how is she to distinguish them from those of another mother? To believe her capable of such feats of clairvoyance and memory in the immensity of the open fields would be midsummer madness.

Never, I say, did I detect a mother permanently posted beside the eggs which she had fastened to a leaf. Further, the total emission is split up into partial deposits dispersed at random, so that the whole tribe comprises a series of clans encamped here and there, often removed to considerable distances which it is impossible to specify.

To rediscover these flocks at the time of the hatching, which falls earlier or later according to the date of production and the degree of exposure to the sun; then, from all over the country-side, to gather into one herd the whole of her very frail and short-legged offspring: this were an obvious impossibility. Let us nevertheless suppose that, by a stroke of good fortune, one of these groups is found and recognized and that the mother devotes herself to it. The others are necessarily abandoned. They thrive none the less well for that. Why, then, should some of the young Bugs be so strangely favoured by maternal solicitude while the majority are able to do without it? Such peculiarities make one suspicious.

De Geer speaks of groups of twenty. These, we are forced to believe, were not the complete family, but detachments sprung from a partial laying. A Pentatoma smaller than the Grey Bug has given me, in one single deposit, more than a hundred eggs. This fecundity must be the general rule where the mode of life is the same. Apart from the twenty watched, then, what became of the rest, left to their own devices?

With all due respect to the Swedish naturalist, the tender cares of the mother Bug and the unnatural appetites of the father eating his children must be relegated to the fairy-tales with which history is crammed. I can obtain, in my breeding-cages, as many hatchings as I wish. The parents are close at hand, under the same cover. What do they do respectively in the presence of the little ones?

Nothing whatever: the fathers do not hasten to slaughter their brats nor do the mothers hasten to their rescue. They wander to and fro on the wire trellis; they take their rest in the restaurant provided by a tuft of rosemary; they pass through the groups of new-born Bugs and topple them over, without evil intent, but also without the least consideration. They are so small, the poor little wretches, and so feeble! A passer-by who grazes them with the tip of his foot turns them over on their backs. Like overturned Tortoises, they vainly kick and wriggle; no one heeds them.

Come then, O devoted mother! Since your family is beset by the danger of capsizing and other disagreeable accidents, place yourself at their head; lead them, step by step, into peaceful pastures; cover them with the buckler of your wing-cases! Any one waiting to observe these beautiful actions, these admirable and edifying moral characteristics, will waste his time and his patience. In three months of diligent watching I never saw, on the part of my charges, any action which in any way suggested the maternal solicitude so often extolled by the compilers of history.

Nature the universal nurse, *alma parens rerum*, is infinitely tender in her treatment of the germs, the treasure of the future; she is a harsh step-mother to the parent. As soon as the creature is capable of supporting itself, she delivers it without pity to life's cruel schooling, which teaches it to resist in the fierce struggle for existence. At first a tender mother, she gives the Pentatoma a delightful casket with a sealed lid to guard the budding flesh from harm; she caps the tiny insect with a mechanical device to set it free, a masterpiece of delicate ingenuity; and then, a stern schoolmistress, she says to the little one:

"I am leaving you. You must now fend for yourself in the hurly-burly of the world."

And the little insect does fend for itself. I see the new-born Bugs, pressed close against one another, remaining for some days on the patch of empty egg-shells. Their flesh grows firmer and their colouring brighter. Mothers pass at no great distance: none of them pays any attention to the drowsy company.

When hunger comes, one of the little ones moves away from the group in search of a canteen; the others follow; they love to feel shoulder touching shoulder, like grazing Sheep. The first to move draws the whole band after him; they make their way in a flock to the tender spots where they insert their suckers and drink their fill; whereupon all return to their native village, seeking a resting-place on the tops of the empty eggs. These expeditions in common are repeated within an increasing radius, till at last, having grown a little stronger, the community, becoming emancipated, makes off and disperses, no longer returning to the place of its birth. Henceforth each lives as he pleases.

What would happen if, when the flock is moving about, a mother were encountered, slow-stepping as the sober Bugs so often are? The little ones, I fancy, would confidently follow their chance-met leader as they follow those among themselves who are the first to make a start. We should then see something like the Hen at the head of her Chicks; accident would give all the appearance of maternal solicitude to a stranger quite indifferent to the mob of brats at her heels.

The worthy De Geer, it seems to me, must have been deceived by such meetings as these, in which maternal care played no part whatever. A little colouring, by way of involuntary adornment, completed the picture; and since then the domestic virtues of the Grey Bug have been lauded in all the books.

1 Cf. *The Glow-worm and Other Beetles*: chaps. xviii. and xix.—*Translator's Note.*

2 For the Nut-weevil, cf. *The Life of the Weevil*, by J. Henri Fabre, translated by Alexander Teixeira de Mattos: chap. vi; also his *Social Life in the Insect World*, translated by Bernard Miall.—*Translator's Note.*

3 Baron Karl de Geer (1720–1778), author of *Mémoires pour servir à l'histoire des insectes.—Translator's Note.*

4 René Antoine Ferchault de Réaumur (1683–1757), author of *Mémoires pour servir à l'histoire naturelle des insectes* and inventor of the Réaumur thermometer-scale.—*Translator's Note.*

5 Or Burying-beetle. Cf. *The Glow-worm and Other Beetles*: chaps. xi and xii.—*Translator's Note.*

CHAPTER II
THE MASKED BUG

I met with this insect unexpectedly and in circumstances that hardly seemed to promise an interesting discovery. A certain enquiry into the spoilers of dead meat, an enquiry set forth elsewhere,1 had brought me to the village butcher's. What will not one do in the hope of securing an idea! The hunt after this rare quarry led me to the workshop of the slaughterer, an excellent man, for that matter, who did me the honours of his establishment to the best of his ability.

I wanted to see not the actual shop, so hateful to look upon, but the shed or what not in which the offal was collected. The butcher took me to the garret, dimly lit by a dormer-window which was left open night and day, in all weathers, to air the place. Continuous ventilation was not unwelcome in that nauseous atmosphere, above all at the hottest time of year, when my visit was paid. The mere recollection of that garret is revolting to my senses.

Here, on a stretched cord, some blood-stained sheepskins are drying; in one corner is a heap of stinking tallow, in another are bones, horns and hoofs. These rags and tatters of death answer my purpose capitally. Under the shovelfuls of fat which I turn over, the Dermestes and her grub are swarming by the thousand; Clothes-moths flit indolently to and fro; and Flies with big red eyes keep on buzzing in and out of the hollow bones that still hold a little marrow. I expected this population, the habitual inmates of carrion refuse. But here is one which I did not anticipate: On the whitewashed wall are certain black patches of unsightly insects, gathered in motionless groups. Among them I recognize the Masked Bug, or Masked Reduvius (*R. personatus*, LIN.), a large Bug of some celebrity. There are nearly a hundred of them, divided into separate flocks.

The butcher watches me as I capture my discovery and put it into a box, and is surprised to see me fearlessly handling the repulsive creature. It is more than he would ever venture to do.

"It comes and plasters itself against the wall," he tells me, "and there it stays. If I sweep it off, next day it's back, as sure as fate. I don't say it does any harm. It doesn't spoil my hides, it doesn't touch my fats. What does it come here for every summer? I don't know."

"I don't know either," I reply, "but I shall try to find out; and, when I know, I can tell you about it, if you'd like me to. It may have something to do with the preservation of your hides. We shall see."

Behold me then, as I leave this offal-store, the shepherd of a chance-met flock. They are not much to look at. Covered with dust, black as pitch, flat, like the true Bugs that they are, standing awkwardly high on their legs, lanky and skinny: no, they do not inspire confidence. The head is so small that there is only just room for the eyes, reticulated domes whose great prominence seems to indicate good powers of vision by night. It is set on an absurd neck which looks as though it had been strangled with a bow-string. The corselet is jet-black, with burnished prominences.

Let us turn it over. The beak is monstrous. Its base covers all of the face that is not occupied by the eyes. It is not the usual rostrum, the drill of the sap-sucking Hemiptera; it is a rude implement, an elbowed tool, crooked like a bent forefinger. What can the creature do with this barbarous weapon? When it is feeding I see a black thread, as fine as a hair, issuing from the beak. This is the slender scalpel: the rest is the sheath and the stout handle. This rude equipment tells us that the Reduvius is an executioner.

What sort of exploits can we expect from it? Stabbing and murdering: actions of little interest, because of their frequency. But we must make a considerable allowance for the unexpected; interesting details sometimes lie dormant and spring up suddenly amid squalid surroundings. Perhaps the Reduvius has in store for us facts worthy of record. Let us try to rear him.

His weapon, a stout yataghan, tells us that the Reduvius is a murderer. What victim does he require? This is the rearing problem before us. It so happens that some time ago I saw the dingy-looking Bug at grips with the smallest of our Cetoniæ, so well-named the Pall-bearing Cetonia,2 because of her white spots on a black background. This accidental observation sets me on the right track. I house my flock in a large glass jar with a bed of sand, and as food I serve up the Cetonia aforesaid, which is common in spring on the flowers in the enclosure, but scarce at this time of year. The victim is very readily accepted. Next day I find her dead. One of the Reduvii, with his probe implanted in the joint of the neck, is working at the corpse and draining it dry.

In the absence of Cetoniæ I fall back upon any sort of game suited to the size of my boarders; and I find that any sort answers my purpose, irrespective of the different entomological orders. The usual dish, because it is the easiest for me to capture, consists of Locusts of medium size, though they are sometimes larger than the consumer. Often, too, for the same reason that he is easily obtained, it includes a Forest Bug, *Pentatoma nigricorna*. In short, my charges' diet does not give me much trouble: anything will do, provided that the prey does not exceed the powers of the assailant.

I was anxious to witness the attack, but I never managed to do so. As the big, prominent eyes of the Reduvius warned me, it takes place at night, at unseasonable hours. However early my inspection, I find the game lifeless, bereft of all power of movement. The hunter is feasting upon his prey and lingers over it for some part of the morning. Then, after many different applications of the probe, now at one point and now at another, when the victims are completely drained of moisture, the blood-suckers abandon the dead bodies, gather into a flock, and do not move all day long, lying flat on the sand at the bottom of the jar. On the following night, if I renew the victuals, the same massacres are repeated.

When the prey is a non-armoured insect, a Locust, for example, I have sometimes noted pulsations in the victim's abdomen. Death, therefore, is not sudden and overwhelming; nevertheless, the quarry must be very quickly made incapable of resistance.

I have confronted the Reduvius with a big-jawed Decticus, a Platycleis3 five or six times the size of his executioner. Next day the colossus was sucked dry by the dwarf as quickly as a Fly would have been. A terrible stab had paralysed him. Where was the blow delivered and how did it take effect?

There is nothing to tell us that the Reduvius is a bravo versed in the art of murder, acquainted, like the Paralysing Wasps, with the anatomy of his victims and the secrets of their nerve-centres. No doubt he drives his stiletto at random into any part where the skin is soft enough. He kills by injecting venom. His rostrum is a poisoned dagger, like that of the Gnat, but much more virulent.

It is said, indeed, that the Masked Bug's bite is painful. Wishing myself to test its effects, so that I might speak with authority, I have tried, but in vain, to get myself bitten. When placed on my finger and pestered, the insect refused to unsheath its weapon. Frequent handling of my specimens, without the use of tweezers, was no more successful. On the evidence of others, then, and not from my own experience, I believe the Reduvius' bite to be a serious matter.

It must be so, intended as it is to kill, swiftly an insect that is not always devoid of vigour. To the victim surprised when asleep it must mean the shooting pain and sudden numbness which the Wasp's sting would produce. The blow is struck here or there, at random. It is possible that the bandit, once the wound has been inflicted, keeps his distance for a while and waits for the limbs to cease kicking before sitting down to devour the corpse. Spiders who have caught a dangerous prey in their webs are wont to take this precaution. They withdraw a little to one side and await the last convulsions of the fettered victim.

Though the details of the murder escape me, I know how the dead insect is exploited. I can witness the performance any morning, as often as I wish. The Reduvius projects from the clumsy scabbard, crooked like a forefinger, a delicate black lancet, which is at once a probe and a suction-pump. The implement is driven into any point of the victim's body, provided that it be covered with skin. Then comes absolute immobility; the banqueter does not budge.

Meanwhile the lancets of the sucker are working, sliding one against the other, acting as a pump, imbibing the victim's life-blood. In like fashion the Cicada drinks the sap of her tree. When she has drained one part of the bark, she moves on and sinks another well. The Reduvius does the same; he drains his prey at several points. He goes from the back of the head to the abdomen, from the abdomen to the neck, from the neck to the thorax and the joints of the legs. Everything is done economically.

I watch with interest the tactics of a Bug exploiting his Locust. Twenty times over I see him changing his point of attack and stopping for a longer or shorter time according to the wealth encountered. He ends up with a haunch, attacked at the joint. The barrel is emptied of its juices until it becomes translucent. If the quarry's skin is diaphanous, the same degree of exhaustion may be perceived throughout the body. Thanks to the action of the infernal pump, a young Praying Mantis an inch long becomes transparent as a moulted skin.

These blood-sucking appetites remind me of our Bed-bug, who makes himself so obnoxious by exploring the sleeper, selecting a convenient spot, leaving it for another and a more profitable, and again moving on, until, swollen to the size of a currant, he withdraws at the first glimmer of daylight. The Reduvius aggravates this method: he first benumbs his victim and then drains it dry. Only the legendary vampire of romance achieves a like degree of frightfulness.

Now, what was the insect-sucker doing in a butcher's loft? He certainly did not find there the victims which I procure for him: Locusts, young Mantes, Grasshoppers, Chrysomelæ,4 all lovers of foliage and the sunlight. These passionate lovers of open-air joys would never venture into the dark and nauseating offal-store. What, then, do these black squads clinging to the wall live upon? Such a crowd needs food, and plenty of it. Where is it?

In the heap of fats, of course! Here a Dermestes (*D. Frischii*, KUGEL)5 swarms promiscuously with her hairy larvæ. The supply is inexhaustible, and it is probably that the Reduvii hastened hither attracted by this abundance. Let us then change the bill of fare, let us substitute Dermestes.

I have just what is needed at my disposal without rushing off to the butcher's for a supply. In the garden, at this moment, supported on reed tripods, there are certain aerial retting-vats in which Moles, Snakes, Lizards, Toads, Fish and so on attract interminable visits from the undertakers of the neighbourhood. The most numerous is a Dermestes, precisely the same as the one in the tallow-loft. This is the very thing I want.

I serve this Dermestes to my Reduvii, I serve him up lavishly. A frenzied massacre takes place. Every morning the sand in the jar is strewn with corpses, many of which are still lying beneath the murderer's beak. The conclusion is obvious: the Reduvius kills the Dermestes whenever the opportunity occurs; without having an exclusive taste for this sort of game, he bleeds it, more or less eagerly, when he comes across it.

I shall communicate this result to the worthy fellow to whom I owe the ingredients of this story. I shall tell him:

"Leave them alone, the ugly creatures whom you see sleeping on the walls of your loft; don't drive them away with your broom. They are doing you a service; they wage war upon the others, the Dermestes, who are so destructive to hides."

It may well be that the abundance of Dermestes, an easy prey, was not the motive which attracted the Reduvii to the butcher's garret. Elsewhere, out of doors, there is no lack of game, in great variety and no less appreciated. Why do the Bugs prefer to gather here? I suspect that they wish to establish a family. The laying-season cannot be far away; and the Reduvius has come with the particular object of providing food and lodging for her offspring. In fact, at the end of June I obtain the first eggs in my jars. For a fortnight the Bugs continue to lay abundantly. A few mothers, reared separately, enable me to estimate their fecundity. I count up thirty to forty eggs for each mother.

Here we no longer see the orderliness dear to the Forest-bugs, who arrange their eggs on a leaf so methodically, in rows of beads. Far from representing an extremely accurate piece of work, the Masked Bug's batch of eggs is strewn, clumsily, at random. The eggs are isolated, adhering neither to one another nor to their support. In my rearing-jars they are scattered over the surface of the sand. Granular specks of which the mother has taken no care whatever, not even troubling to fasten them anywhere, they roll hither and thither, at the least breath of air. A plant is not more heedless of its seeds, which go where the wind blows them.

These greatly neglected eggs are nevertheless not without beauty of form; they are oval, amber-red, smooth and glossy and about a millimetre[6] in length. Near one of the ends there is a fine, dark, circular line, marking a sort of cap. The Forest-bug's egg has taught us the meaning of this circle. It is the line along which the lid of the casket will open. We have before us for the second time the tiny miracle of an egg shaped like a casket, which, on hatching, opens without breaking, by the fall of a little lid which is thrust back by the tiny creature in the act of birth.

If I can manage to see how the moveable cap is lifted, I shall obtain the most interesting detail of the Masked Bug's history; I shall have the equivalent of the young Forest-bug bursting the ceiling of his shell by means of a sharp-angled mitre actuated by the hydraulic pulsations of the head. Let us stint neither time nor patience: the exodus of a Bug from his egg is a most notable sight.

If the problem has its attractive side, it also presents difficulties. You have to be on the spot just at the very moment when the lid gives way, which entails a wearisome vigilance. You also want plenty of light; and it must be daylight, or the refinements of this very delicate operation would escape us. The habits of the Reduvius give me cause to fear that the eggs may be hatched at night: [And the future will teach me only too well how fully my fears are founded.] No matter: we will not give in. Perhaps fortune will smile upon me. And, lens in hand, for a fortnight, at all hours, from morning to night, I keep watch over a hundred eggs which I have divided among several glass tubes.

In the Forest-bug's egg the approach of hatching is announced by a black line in the form of a broad arrow, or reversed anchor, which appears not far from the lid and is no other than the liberating mechanism. The tiny beast covers its head with its pointed mitre. Here there is nothing of the sort. From first to last, the Masked Bug's egg retains its uniform amber colouring, without any sign of an inner lock.

Meanwhile, by the middle of July, the hatchings are becoming numerous. Every morning I find in my tubes a collection of tiny open pots, unbroken and amber-coloured as at the beginning. The lid, a concave dome of exquisite accuracy, is lying on the sand beside the empty egg-shell; sometimes it remains hanging from the edge of the orifice. The young Bugs, pretty little snow-white creatures, are gambolling nimbly amidst the untenanted pots. I always come too late; what I wanted to see by sunlight is over.

As I suspected, the opening of the lid is effected in the darkness of the night. Alas, for want of sufficient light the solution of the problem which interests me so greatly will escape me! The Reduvius will keep her secret; I shall see nothing.... But yes, I do see something; for perseverance has unexpected resources. A week full of failures has already gone by, when, unexpectedly, in the brilliant light of nine o'clock in the morning, a few late-comers suddenly begin to open their boxes. Had the house caught fire just then, I doubt whether I should have stirred a limb. The sight held me rooted to the floor. Let the reader judge for himself.

Unprovided with the thread-like rivets employed by the Pentatoma, the Reduvius' lid adheres to the shell by its mere position and a perfect fit. I see it lifting at one side and hinging on the other with a slowness that defies the magnifying powers of the lens. What is happening in the egg seems to be a long and laborious process. But the lid opens wider; and through the chink I see something glistening. This is an iridescent pellicle, which protrudes and, as it does so, pushes back the lid. Now a spherical blister emerges from the shell, gradually growing larger, like a soap-bubble blown from a straw. Pushed farther and farther back by the expansion of this bladder, the lid falls off.

Then the bomb explodes: that is to say, the capsule, inflated beyond the limits of its resistance, bursts open at the top. This envelope, an extremely thin membrane, usually adheres to the edge of the orifice, where it forms a high white rim. At other times the explosion detaches it and shoots it out of the shell. Under these conditions it is a delicate goblet, hemispherical, with torn edges, and with its lower part continued by a fine, twisted stem.

It is finished; the thoroughfare is open. The tiny insect can now emerge by bursting through the pellicle caught in the opening, or by dislodging it, or it may find an absolutely free passage, when the burst bladder has left the egg. It is all simply miraculous. To escape from his box, the Pentatoma invented the three-ribbed mitre and the hydraulic ram; the Reduvius has invented the explosive bomb. The first goes to work gently; the second, a brutal dynamiter, blows the roof off his prison with a bomb.

With what explosive, and how is the liberating shell loaded? At the moment of rupture nothing visible bursts from the bubble; nothing liquid moistens the torn edge. The contents, therefore, were assuredly gaseous. The rest escapes me. One observation, which I was unable to repeat, is not enough in this delicate matter. Reducing it to mere probabilities I will propose the following explanation:

The tiny animal is wrapped in a tightly closed tunic which embraces it snugly. This is a temporary skin, a sheath which the new-born larva will shed on leaving the egg. This sheath is connected with an appendage, a capsule placed under the lid. The twisted stem hanging from the burst bubble when it is shot out of the egg represents the communicating duct.

Very slowly, as the little creature takes shape and grows, this bladder-like reservoir receives the products of the respiration which takes place under the cover of the tunic or "overall." Instead of dispersing outside, through the egg-shell, the carbonic acid gas incessantly resulting from the vital process of oxidization accumulates in this sort of gasometer, filling and distending it and pressing upon the lid. When the little Bug is mature and on the point of hatching, the increased activity of its respiration completes the inflation, which has doubtless been proceeding ever since the earliest development of the germ. At last, yielding to the increasing pressure of the gas-filled capsule, the lid becomes unfastened. The Chick in its shell has its air-chamber: the young Reduvius has its bomb of carbonic acid gas: it releases itself by breathing.

The singular hatching-processes of the Pentatoma and the Reduvius are obviously not isolated cases. The egg with a removable lid must be employed by other Hemiptera; it may even be that this is a fairly general device. Each genus has its own methods of opening its box, its own system of springs and levers. What a mechanism to find in the egg of a Bug, and how fertile in surprises! What an interesting harvest to be reaped, with patience and a good pair of eyes!

Let us now watch the little Reduvius' emergence. The lid fell off a few moments ago. The tiny insect, white all over, comes forth, tightly swaddled. The tip of its abdomen still remains within the opening, which, with its rim of skin, the remnant of the bomb, serves it as a supporting girdle. It struggles, swaying to and fro and leaning backwards. This gymnastic exercise, increasing the creature's flexibility, is intended to undo the swaddling-clothes at the seams. Sleeves, breeches, gaiters, shirt-front, cap: little by little the whole is torn off, not without effort on the fettered pigmy's part; it is all cast aside and disappears in tatters. Behold the new-born insect at liberty! It skips away to some distance from the egg. With its long, fine, waving antennæ it interrogates space, enquiring into this mighty world. Often, when the lid still adheres to some point of the opening, it carries this bit away with it, on its back or its rump. You would think it was going to the wars, bearing the *umbo* of antiquity, the round, convex buckler. What does it want with this armour? Has it seized upon it as a means of defence? Not at all. The cover of the beaker happened to come into contact with it and at once stuck to it, even firmly, for nothing short of the approaching moult will detach the disk. This detail tells us that the little creature exudes a fluid capable of acting as an adhesive in respect of any light objects encountered on its passage—with what results we shall presently see.

With shield on back or without this panoply, standing high on its legs and sporting a long pair of horns, the new-born insect crosses the threshold of the egg; it roams about in sudden fits and starts, presenting the appearance of a minute Spider. Two days later, before taking any food, it undergoes a moult. The gormandizer, once he has eaten his fill, undoes a button to make room for the belated dainties concluding the meal. The Bug, who has as yet eaten nothing, splits his coat from top to bottom, throws it away, and puts on a new skin. He even changes his belly before sitting down to table. He used to wear a short, stumpy abdomen; he now has a plump, round paunch. The time has come for feasting.

A restaurant-keeper with no experience of the proper bill of fare, what shall I provide? I remember a passage in Linnæus7 touching the Reduvius. The master says:

"*Consumit cimices lectularios huius larva, horrida, personata.*" "Its horrid, masked larva sucks the Bed-bugs."

This game seems to me out of proportion for the moment: the little creatures in my jars, weak and tiny as they are, would never dare to tackle such a quarry. There is another objection: the moment I want Bugs, I am unlikely to find any. Let us try something else.

The adult has eclectic tastes; it hunts the most varied prey. The larva might well do likewise. I offer Midges. They are absolutely refused. In the garret whence my flock originated, what could they have found that was easily obtained, without scuffling, so dangerous at that tender age? They would have found tallow, bones, hides, and nothing else. Let us give them tallow.

This time all goes well. My little creatures settle down on the fatty substance, driving their suckers into it, drinking deeply of the stinking olein, and then retire to digest their meal in the sand, wherever they please. They thrive. I see them growing from day to day. In a fortnight they are plump, and, what is more, disguised beyond recognition. Their whole bodies, including the legs, are encrusted with sand.

This mineral bark began to form directly after the moult. The little creatures became speckled with earthy particles, thinly scattered at random. At present the envelope is continuous. Let matters take their course, and this wrap will become a sordid overall. Then the larva will really deserve the epithets which Linnæus bestows upon it: *horrida, personata,* the horrible insect that dons a mask and wears a dusty domino.

Should it occur to us to regard this tatter-demalion costume as an intentional piece of work, a *ruse de guerre,* a means of dissimulation whereby to approach its prey, we may undeceive ourselves: the Reduvius does not industriously make itself an overcoat; nor does it wear one with the object of concealing itself. It all happens of itself, without any sort of art, like the mechanism whose secret was revealed to us by the lid of the egg, worn as a buckler. The insect exudes a certain unctuous humour, derived perhaps from the tallow on which it feeds. To this varnish, the dust through which it passes adheres without any further trouble on the insect's part. The Reduvius does not dress itself; it dirties itself; it turns into a pellet of dust, a walking bit of filth, because it emits a sticky sweat.

One word more as to its diet. Linnæus, obtaining his information I know not where, makes the Reduvius our auxiliary against the Bed-bug. Since then, the books, monotonously echoing one another, have repeated the eulogy; it is accepted as a tradition that the Masked Reduvius makes war upon our nocturnal bloodsucker. This would certainly constitute a magnificent claim on our gratitude. But is it really the truth? I take the liberty of rebelling against tradition. That the Reduvius is sometimes found slaying Bed-bugs is very likely: my own captives were satisfied with Forest-bugs. They accepted them, however, without clamouring for them; and they readily dispensed with them, seeming to prefer Locusts or any other insects.

Let us not then hasten to generalize and to look upon the Reduvius as a licensed consumer of the stinking pest of our beds. I see an important objection to this special vocation. Comparatively large in size, the Reduvius could not slip into the narrow chinks that shelter the Bed-bug. *A fortiori*, to track the Bed-bug to its lair is impracticable for the larva, hampered by its overcoat of dust, unless it invade our beds at the time when the other is running over us and selecting its morsel. Nothing justifies our presuming this intimacy with the sleeper; no one, that I know of, has surprised the Reduvius or its larva in the act of investigating our beds.

The masked larva does not deserve to be extolled for a few accidental captures. Its diet is quite different from what Linnæus tells us and the compilers keep on repeating. In its infancy it feeds on fatty matters, as my rearing-experiments prove. When it grows big it varies its victuals with insects, of no matter what order, as does the adult. For it a butcher's garret is an abode of bliss, where it finds a supply of fats, and, later, Flesh-flies, Dermestes, and other insects that batten on dead things. In the dark and ill-swept corners of our houses it gleans the particles of fat that fall from our kitchen-table; it catches unawares the drowsy Fly, the small, homeless Spider. This is enough to ensure its welfare.

Here is one more tradition to be deleted from our books, without much injury, however, to the insect's reputation. If the Masked Bug ceases to appear in history as the executioner of the Bed-bug, it will henceforth cut a more respectable figure as the inventor of the box that is opened by the explosion of a bomb.

1 For the Bluebottle cf. *The Life of the Fly*: chaps. xiv to xvi.—*Translator's Note.*

2 Cf. *More Beetles*: chap. i.—*Translator's Note.*

3 Cf. *The Life of the Grasshopper*: chap. xiii.—*Translator's Note.*

4 Golden Apple-beetles, or Leaf-beetles. Cf. *The Mason-Wasps*, by J. Henri Fabre, translated by Alexander Teixeira de Mattos: chap. viii.—*Translator's Note.*

5 Bacon-beetles. Cf. *More Beetles*: chap. ii.—*Translator's Note.*

6 1⁄25 inch.—*Translators Note.*

7 Carolus Linnæus (Karl von Linné: 1707–1778), the Swedish botanist and naturalist, author of *Systema naturæ*, etc.—*Translator's Note.*

CHAPTER III
THE TEREBINTH-LOUSE: THE GALLS

For curious methods of generation, the Plant-lice bear the palm. Nowhere shall we find anything to beat them unless we pry into the secrets of the sea. We must not look to them for remarkable feats of instinct. The humble, round-bellied Lice are incapable of such achievements; to these stay-at-homes the lifting of a foot spells an excess of emancipation. But they will tell us by what attempts, bewildering in their energy and variety, the universal law that governs the transmission of life has come into being.

I shall consult the Terebinth-lice by preference. They are near neighbours of mine, a condition essential to frequent visits; they practise an industry, which is a not uninteresting addition; and they are crowded into sealed enclosures where we can follow the progress of the family without too much confusion.

The shrub that feeds them, the terebinth, or turpentine-tree, abounds on the Sérignan hills. It is sensitive to the cold, a lover of stony wastes scorched by the sun. Its insignificant flowers are succeeded by pretty bunches of little berries, first pink, then blue, smelling of turpentine and beloved by the Redstart when migrating in autumn.

Any one seeing it for the first time, unless conversant with its history, might think that it bore yet another crop of fruit, quite different from that of the berries. On the tips of the boughs, singly or in bunches, are certain twisted horns, a fairly good imitation of certain pimentos, if the coral-red of maturity were replaced by a straw-yellow washed with rose. What is more, mimic apricots, fresher and more satiny than those of our orchards, are seen hanging from the leaves. Tempted by appearances, we open these deceptive productions. Horror! The contents consist of myriads of Lice, swarming about in the midst of a floury dust.

Pilgrims to the Holy Land tell us that on certain bushes in the neighbourhood of Sodom beautiful-looking apples may be gathered, which are full of ashes within. The pretty apricots and cornute pimentos of the terebinth-tree are the apples of Sodom, the Dead Sea fruit. Beneath an attractive exterior, they too contain nothing but ashes, live ashes, a wriggling whirl of dusty vermin. These are excrescences, galls, in which the opulent family of the Plant-lice lives isolated from the outer world.

To follow the progress of these strange productions I needed a terebinth which I could inspect often and in comfort. I happen to have one a few steps from my door. When I was stocking the enclosure with a certain amount of woody vegetation, I conceived the happy thought of planting a terebinth. A profitable tree, yielding acceptable fruit, would have died in this ungrateful soil; but this, which is good for nothing but firewood, is prospering excellently. It has grown into a magnificent specimen; and year after year it never fails to be covered with galls. So here I am, the fortunate possessor of a tree full of Lice. Let us call it by its Provençal name: *lou Petelin*, or *lou Pesouious*, the lousy one.

Scarcely a day passes but I give it a glance, attracted as I am by the daily happenings in the enclosure. Let us examine it closely. The "lousy one" has its merits: it is the depository of interesting secrets. In winter it is bare. With the foliage the wigwams of Lice have disappeared, though towards the end of the summer they were weighing it down with their numbers. Nothing is left but the horn-shaped shells, now black and dilapidated ruins.

What has become of the vast population of the bush? How will it recover possession of its terebinth? In vain I inspect the bark of the trunk and branches and twigs: I see nothing capable of explaining the coming invasion. Nowhere are there any lice in a state of lethargy, nowhere any eggs awaiting the spring hatching. Nor are there any in the neighbourhood, nor, in particular, in the heap of dead leaves rotting at the foot of the tree. Yet the tiny creature cannot come from a distance: a mere atom, as I see it in imagination, does not go wandering across country. It is certainly on the tree that feeds it; but where?

One day in January, weary of my futile search, it occurs to me to strip off, in shreds, a lichen, the Wall Parmelia, which here and there carpets thinly with its yellow rosettes the base and the thicker branches of my terebinth. I examine my harvest through the lens, in my study. What is this?

A magnificent discovery! In my scrap of lichen, no larger than a finger-nail, I discover a world. On the inner surface, in the winding crevices between the scales, are encrusted vast numbers of tiny red bodies barely a millimetre1 in length. Some of them are entire and oval in shape; some, truncated and empty, display open pouches with pointed ends. All are plainly segmented.

Can it be that I have before my eyes the Louse's eggs, of which some are old and empty, while others are recent and contain their germ? This idea is soon disposed of: an egg has not this segmentation like that of an insect's abdomen. Here is a more significant fact: a head and antennæ are visible in front, while legs may be seen underneath; the whole is dry and brittle. These specks, accordingly, once lived and walked. Are they dead now? No, for when I crush them with the point of a needle traces of moisture gush forth, a sign of a living organism. Only the shell is dead.

The tiny creature, capable at first of movement, endowed with legs and antennæ, wandered for some time under cover of the lichen; then, before it became inert, it settled down on a suitable spot. There it turned its shrivelled skin, now an amber-coloured pellicle, into a mummy's sarcophagus in which the organism makes ready for a new life. When the time comes, we shall discover the origin of this curious object, which was an animal and now deserves the name of egg.

What my own familiar terebinth has shown me in the enclosure, I ought to see repeated in the open country. Sure enough, I do see it; but this time it is not under lichens, for the bark of the tree is most often bare. There is no lack of other shelter. Some twigs of terebinth have been cut by the clumsy bill-hooks of the brushwood-gleaners, leaving a ragged section. The wood is split into deep fissures; the loose bark comes away in tatters. Once dry, these ruins are a mine of wealth.

In the narrowest crevices, in the cracks of the wood and under the splintered bark, there are great numbers of the atoms that interest me so greatly. To judge by their colour there are at least two kinds. Some are red; the others are black. These latter were scarce under the lichens on my terebinth; here they predominate largely. I collect some of both kinds. And now we must have patience. I have hopes that the answer to the riddle will be found.

Mid-April comes and the little glass tubes in which I store my animal seeds are full of life. The black germs are the first to hatch; a fortnight later the red ones follow suit. The epidermic boxes undergo a process of self-mutilation, the front part falling off and leaving a gaping void, without other change of form. A minute animal comes out of them, a black speck in which the lens recognizes a very shapely little Louse, bearing the regulation sucker pressed against its thorax. My first thoughts were correct: the puzzling little red and black bodies found under the lichens and in the cracks of dead wood were really Louse-seeds.

And these seeds, judging by their husks, endowed with a head and legs, are little insects, first active and then inert and converted into germs. The original, almost integral substance is reborn in another shape. The little creature's skin has provided the shell, the segmented box, a jet-black or amber-yellow pellicule; the rest is concentrated into an egg.

The time has not come to observe the singular creature's origin and behaviour; chronological order forbids. Let us return to the vermin issuing from these germs. They are tiny, tiny little black Lice, with flat abdomens, plainly segmented and as it were granular. Assiduous observation through the lens shows them to be dusted with a touch of blue-grey powder like the bloom on a plum. Trotting with little steps about their spacious prison, the glass tube, they seem uneasy. What do they want? What are they looking for? No doubt, a camping-ground on the friendly tree.

I come to their assistance; I place in the tube a twig of terebinth whose buds are beginning to open at the top of their scaly covering. This is the thing they wanted. They climb up the twig, establish themselves in the velvet that clothes the tips of the buds, and there they settle, calm and satisfied.

Direct observations made on the terebinth are accompanied, *pari passu*, by laboratory experiments. The little black Lice, rare on the 15th of April, are numerous ten days later. On the tip of a single bud I count over twenty of them; and most of the buds are colonized, or at least those that are largest and farthest from the ground. The occupants remain hidden in the scanty down of the nascent follicles whose tips are barely emerging.

After a sojourn of some days, when the leaves begin to appear, each insect makes for itself a private dwelling. It exploits, with its sucker, a leaflet whose tip turns purple, swells up and curls over, and, bringing its edges together, forms a flat pocket with an irregular opening. Each of these pockets, about the size of a grain of hemp-seed, is a tent in which a black Plant-louse takes up her residence: one only, never more.

What will the little Louse do in her isolated retreat? Feed, and, above all, multiply. If one is to become legion a few months hence, matters brook no delay. Here, then, there is no father, a mere superfluity and waste of time. So many Lice, so many mothers; no more is needed. Nor is there any laying, for the egg would take too long to develop. Nothing short of direct procreation, unfettered by any preliminaries, is acceptable to the Louse's ardour. The young are born alive and like their mother, except in point of size.

As soon as they are brought into the world, they insert their suckers, absorb a little sap, increase in size, and in a few days become capable of continuing the race by the same rapid method, without fathers. Until the end of the annual colonization the offspring, including the remotest degrees of descent, will maintain the process of genesis by direct parturition and will know no other method. When the time has come for a more convenient examination, we shall return to this amazing method, which completely upsets our ideas.

On the 1st of May I open some of the purple swellings which have formed on the tips of the burgeoning leaflets. Sometimes I find the maker of the capsule alone, just as she was on the tips of the buds; sometimes she has undergone a moult and is accompanied by the beginnings of a family. After discarding her black slough, she has become greenish, corpulent and lightly dusted with flour. Her youngsters, at the moment one or at most two, are brown, slender and bare-skinned.

In order to follow the progress of the family, I place under a glass a couple of capsules which so far contain only the founder. Two days later I have a dozen young Lice, who soon desert the natal pocket and make for the cotton-wool closing the glass tube. This hasty migration indicates that the young Lice have their function elsewhere, on the tender, already unfolded leaves. Detached from its fostering support, the little purple cell dries up and its inhabitant dies. My census can no longer be continued. No matter: I have learnt that one day is enough to produce three births. If this birth-rate persists for a fortnight, the maker of the capsule will have brought forth a handsome family, gradually scattered over the wide field of exploitation offered by the terebinth.

A fortnight later the red eggs hatch out, when the young twigs are already shooting and unfolding their leaves. As far as I could judge from my highly unreliable observations of these swarming insects, which are not clearly distinguishable one from the other, the later generation begins as did the earlier. It causes purple nodules to appear on the tips of the leaflets, little wallets similar in shape and size to a grape-stone. Like those already mentioned, these cells are inhabited at first by a single Plant-louse.

In both cases the rage for rapid multiplication is the same. The recluses soon produce offspring, who desert the natal shelter and proceed to settle elsewhere as colonists. At last, its flanks drained dry, the viviparous little insect dies in its withered arbour.

How many were they, coming from under the lichens and climbing to the assault of the terebinth? There were thousands of them; and this multitude is not enough. Hastily each Louse attacks her leaflet with her beak; she makes herself a lair out of its swollen tip and immediately gives birth to other Lice, multiplying ten- or perhaps a hundredfold in this invasion of the innumerable. The tree has now its full number of colonists, all capable of founding populous tribes.

Are we to regard them as different branches of the same trade union, of the same family, exploiting the terebinth in various fashions, according to the point attacked? We hesitate to regard them as strangers to one another, when they are employed on the same work; yet there are significant reasons for concluding that we have here a duality or multiplicity of species.

Besides the disparity of the work accomplished, there is, at the outset, one distinctive feature: the colour of the eggs, of which some are black and others red. These vividly contrasted hues must correspond with independent ancestries. It is even possible that a patient examination, capable of analysing this minute object, would find differences in husks of the same colour. All my own searches beneath patches of lichen and in the crevices of dead wood end in nothing more than the discovery of two sorts of ovular carapaces but of two only, at least to judge by appearances; and yet on the tree we shall find five categories of workers who, though resembling one another, build very dissimilar structures. If there are no other germs, germs which have escaped my careful observation, it would seem, therefore that the eggs have different contents under an identical shell, whether black or red.

Lastly, the configuration, that essential characteristic of the species, displays, in late autumn, very emphatic differentiating features. Up to this late season, the inmates of the galls of every form are so much alike that it is impossible to distinguish them one from another once they are taken from their dwellings. When the final exodus comes, at the close of the year, a generation makes its appearance which differs greatly from its predecessors, giving final proof of multiple species, to the number of five.

Their generic name is *Pemphigus,* which is to say, bubble, capsule, bladder. This scientific name is well deserved. The Terebinth-lice and some others that pursue similar callings, living on the elm and the poplar, are, in a word, artificers of swellings: by the incessant tickling of their suckers they cause the formation of hollow excrescences, which are at once board and lodging to the community.

On the terebinth, the simplest of these dwellings consists of a lateral fold of the leaf, the edge of which is turned back over the upper surface and fastened to it without losing its green colour. This hem gives a very low-roofed dwelling: the floor and the ceiling meet. Therefore, being unduly confined, the family is not numerous. The timid maker of these green hems bears the name of *Pemphigus pallidus,* DERB. She is called pale because she has not the knack of painting her house purple.

Elsewhere the lateral fold, still turned over the upper surface of the leaf, grows much thicker, swells with fleshy tissue, develops wrinkles, assumes a crimson hue and becomes a short, hollow, spindle-shaped growth. This home, a fairly successful imitation of the seed-pods of the peony and the larkspur, belongs to the *Pemphigus follicularius,* PASS.

Elsewhere again the fold, which at first is made in the plane of the leaf, is now bent down at right angles under the leaf, becoming an ear-shaped appendage, a knotted, fleshy crescent, with a straw-yellow as its prevailing colour. This is the work of the *Pemphigus semilunaris,* PASS.

The spherical galls take higher rank in the Plant-louse's art. They are smooth, pale-yellow globes, varying in size from that of a cherry to that of an average apricot. They hang from the base of the leaves, which, despite these monstrous bladders, retain their normal colour, and, in all other respects, their normal shape. The insect which inflates these pretty capsules is *Pemphigus utricularius*, PASS.

But the most remarkable structures are the horn-shaped galls, truly Cyclopean monuments compared with their minute builders. Some attain a length of nine inches and are as thick as the neck of a claret-bottle. Grouped in threes or fours at the tips of the upper branches, they form barbaric trophies, twisted and fantastic danger-signals which might have graced the brows of some Alpine Ibex.

The other galls all fall off with the leaves; not a trace of them remains on the tree in winter, and even these firmly cemented to their bough, last for a long time. Only the protracted assaults of wind and weather will destroy them completely. The base itself does not easily disappear. Next year it is still in its place, but dilapidated and reduced to the broken stump of a horn of plenty packed with the waxy felt that clothed the population in the days of its prosperity. In these palaces lived *Pemphigus cornicularius*, PASS.

The purple pitchers of the first phase are provisional stations in which the Lice prepare for wholesale colonization. Each of these humble cottages has its Plant-louse from the foot of the tree. The solitary, who was herself hatched from a germ, makes haste to give birth to live youngsters, who gradually spread over the new leaves, and die. Then the true galls come, the great cities which will provide room for several generations. Here again, all the five classes of specialists between whom we have discriminated set to work, all labouring independently at the first filling out of the cabins. Mutual assistance will come later.

May arrives; and already the simpler galls begin to grow: the lateral folds which, bent back upon the edge, become so many green hems. Beneath the awl of the black Louse, patiently pricking away at the leaf, a narrow border curves inwards from the edge. The line of attack measures a couple of centimetres.2 When it has worked long enough at this or that point, the tiny insect changes its place and goes elsewhere to begin all over again, standing motionless while its implement performs its functions.

Now what is the atom doing thus to warp what would be flat under natural conditions? Merely implanting its sucker. The prick of a needle, however skilfully guided, would bruise the tissues without affecting their form. The little insect must therefore instil a certain virus, which provokes an exaggerated flow of sap; it injects an irritant poison and the plant reacts by the swelling of the wounded parts.

And now the hem is growing wider, with a slowness that defies our scouting: as well try to follow with the eyes the growth of a blade of grass.

It is now a slanting roof, a gaping fold. The Louse is in the angle, at her post, doing her duty as a turncock. With her fine probe she stimulates and controls the flow of sap. In twenty-four hours the roof completes its descent, pressing tightly against the leaf. It is a lowered trap-door; but the mechanism of the structure works with such caution that the tiny insect, far from being crushed between the two thicknesses of leaf, retains its liberty of movement and moves about inside the fold as it would do in the open air.

A curious instrument, the awl of the little black Louse! With our modern machinery a child's finger, applied to this or that lever, this or that valve, sets enormous masses in motion. Similarly, the Louse, with her delicate probe, sets powerful hydraulic machinery going and trims the sails of a leaflet. She is, after her fashion, an engineer on a gigantic scale.

The spindle- or ear-shaped galls make their first appearance on the edge of the leaves in the form of narrow crimson borders. Soon the walls grow thicker and become gnarled and fleshy, expanding into excrescences from which all green is excluded.

How is it that the part of the leaf treated by the Louse is naturally yellow and crimson, when, if simply folded, it retains its normal green hue unimpaired? Again, how is it that in the one case the thickness of the tissues is not increased while in the other it becomes augmented? Why does the spindle keep to the plane of the edge, whereas the ear-shaped gall, or auricle, abruptly bends its leaf and hangs vertically? In all three cases, the implement is the same and the work differs profoundly. Is it the effect of a virus whose properties vary according to the sucker that inoculates it? Is it the result of a change of method in wielding the awl? We are confounded.

The problem becomes doubly obscure when we consider the spherical galls. Here the original black Louse settles just at the base of a leaf, on the upper surface, against the median vein. There she takes her stand, motionless and patient. The point abraded by the awl is hollowed into a tiny pit, which soon forms a small protuberance beneath the underside of the leaf. As though its foothold were gradually withdrawn, the insect dives and is swallowed up by a pocket whose opening closes of its own accord by the contact of its lips.

Here we have the Plant-louse at home, strictly isolated from the world. Though the edge of the fostering leaflet undergoes no alteration of shape or colour, the pitcher-shaped appendage at its base turns a pale yellow and grows larger day by day, thanks to the centrifugal expansion provoked by the insect's irritant sucker. The continual punctures of the solitary Louse and presently of her offspring will enlarge it, by the end of the summer, to the dimensions of a fair-sized plum.

The horn-shaped galls originate in an entire leaf, selected from among the smallest. On the tops of the boughs there are sickly leaves, the last achievements of an exhausted impulse. Scarcely unfolded and innocent of green, the colour of health, they measure barely a fifth of an inch in length. It is on these vegetable trifles that the enormous horn-shaped structures are based; and even so the leaf is not completely utilized, but only one of its lobes: in short, a speck, a mere nothing.

Exploited by the Plant-louse, this mere nothing acquires a peculiar energy. In the first place, it welds itself to the tip of the twig and becomes one with it, so that it lingers on the tree when the leaves fall and, with them, the other galls; next, it excites a flow of sap comparable with that of the pumpkin-stalk nourishing its fruit. The very small begets the huge. The gall is at first a pretty little horn, regular in shape and green all over. Open it. The interior is a magnificent flesh-colour and soft as satin. For the moment, a solitary Louse, a black one, inhabits this attractive residence.

The five kinds of establishment have been founded, from the fold to the horn; they have only to grow larger as their population increases. Now what are they doing, these Lice immured in solitary confinement, each after her own fashion? To begin with, they are changing their clothes and their shape. They used to be black and slender, suitably built for wandering over the budding leaves: now they adopt sedentary habits, turn yellow and put on flesh. And now, with the sucker implanted on the wall, which is swollen with turpentine, they quietly give birth to their young. For them this is a continuous function, like that of digestion. They have nothing else to do.

Shall we call them fathers? No: the word would clash with the expression "giving birth." Shall we speak of them as mothers? Not that either. The exact meaning of the word prevents us. They are neither one nor the other, nor are they an intermediate form. Our language has no term to describe these animal curiosities. We must resort to the plants to acquire an approximate notion of the whole procedure.

In our parts, the common garlic scarcely ever flowers: cultivation has caused it to lose its sexual duality. It knows nothing of true seed, to which the paternity of the stamen and the maternity of the pistil contribute. Yet the plant multiplies readily enough. The underground part begets its offspring directly, that is to say, it produces large fleshy buds, gathered into a cluster of what is known as cloves. Each is a living embryo plant, which, when buried in the soil, continues its development and grows like the original plant. To multiply the garlic in his kitchen-garden, the gardener has no other resource than that of the cloves, the usual seed being here non-existent.

Some plants of the same alliaceous group are even more remarkable. They send up a normal stem, ending in what appears to be a spherical head of blossom. Properly this head should blossom into an umbel of flowers.

But this is not what happens. There are no flowers whatever; they are replaced by bulbils, a diminutive form of clove. Sexuality has disappeared: instead of seeds, announced by the preparations for flowering, the plant produces plantlets, concentrated into fleshy buds. On the other hand, the underground part has a lavish supply of cloves. Though the garlic is sexless, its future is assured; it will have no lack of successors.

To a certain extent, the genesis of the Plant-louse will bear comparison with that of the garlic. The strange insect also puts forth bulbils: that is to say, it is spared all ovarian delay and procreates live offspring without assistance.

The male is nobler than the female, says Lhomond.3 This is a pedantic formula, generally refuted by natural history. In the animal kingdom, work, industry and ability, those true titles of nobility, are the attributes of the mother. No matter: let us accept Lhomond's dictum; and, since we are allowed the choice, let us speak of the Plant-louse as of the masculine gender, which is the nobler from the grammarian's point of view. For that matter, nothing shall prevent us speaking of it as feminine, if our speech thereby gains in lucidity.

Isolated in his cell, the original Plant-louse, we were saying, grows a new skin and puts on flesh. He brings sons into the world, all of whose beaks play their part in enlarging the gall, while all their bellies are engaged in increasing the population. We are reminded of the avalanche which, at first a mere lump, becomes an enormous mass of snow.

When summer is over, in September, let us open a gall, no matter which, spread out the contents on a sheet of paper, take up a magnifying-glass, and see what there is to see. Folds, spindles, auricles, globes and horns afford us almost the same spectacle, allowing for numbers, which are here restricted and there enormous. The Lice are a magnificent orange yellow. The largest have stumps on their shoulders, the rudiments of wings to be.

All are clad in an exquisite cloak, whiter than snow, which projects some distance behind them, like a train. This finery is a waxy fleece exuded by the skin. It will not bear the touch of a camel-hair brush; a breath destroys it; but the Louse despoiled of it will soon sweat out another. In the crowded gall, where so many individuals are huddled together, jostling one another, the waxen garment is often torn to shreds and pulverized. Hence a collection of floury rags, forming the downiest of beds, in which the tribe lie about.

Mixed higgledy-piggledy with the orange Lice we see others, much less numerous but easily detected. They are smaller, and are sometimes a rusty-red, sometimes a fairly bright vermilion. Always stocky and wrinkled, they are, according to the age and the pattern of the gall, either round as a Tortoise or shaped like a triangle with rounded corners. On their backs, they carry six to eight rows of white tufts, a waxy exudation, like the white smocks of the others. An attentive examination with the magnifying-glass is needed to detect this detail of their costume. They never sport the wing-stumps which the others acquire sooner or later.

One last characteristic, more important than all the rest, places these pigmies in a category completely by themselves. From time to time I see on their backs a monstrous protuberance which mounts as high as the neck and doubles the creature's bulk. Now this hump, which is here to-day and gone to-morrow, only to reappear later, is the conjurer's wallet containing the future. When I manage to open one, without mishap, with the point of a needle, I extract from it a slimy speck displaying two black eye-spots, with traces of segmentation. My Cæsarean operation has laid bare an embryo.

I reserved the right to pass, grammatically, from the masculine to the feminine gender. And this is the time to do so. I isolate a few of the hunch-backed squaws in a small glass tube, with a scrap of gall. They give me young ones; and the humps disappear. The observation, unfortunately, cannot be continued: the scrap of gall withers and my specimens die. None the less it is now established that these pigmy Lice are mothers and that they carry knapsacks on their backs as incubating pockets.

The little red tortoises found in all the galls in the late summer are therefore as prolific as the famous old woman who lived in a shoe: they alone bring forth young. All around them swarm their descendants, fat orange babies, who deck themselves in snow-white furbelows, suck the sap, distend their stomachs and prepare to grow wings in view of an approaching migration.

Are the hunch-backed mothers all the immediate daughters of the black Louse, the founder of the gall, or do they form a lineage at various removes? The latter seems probable in the horn-shaped galls, where the mothers are so exceedingly numerous. A single origin would not account for this prodigality. As for the other, far less thickly-populated galls, it seems to me that a single generation of red Lice would be sufficient.

Let me mention a few approximate figures. In the first week of September I open a horn-shaped gall, selected from among the largest. It measures eight inches in length by nearly an inch and a half in thickness at its greatest diameter. The population consists mainly of orange Lice, plump, smooth, and endowed with wing-stumps. These are the progeny of the tiny mothers. These latter are scarlet, stocky and wrinkled, with their fore-part tapering and their hinder-part as if it were cut off short, so that their shape is almost triangular. As far as I can judge in the confusion of such a multitude, they should number some hundreds.

To estimate the whole population, I pack it into a glass tube eighteen millimetres4 in diameter. The column thus formed occupies a height of 56 millimetres.5 The volume, therefore, amounts to 16,532 cubic millimetres.6 Therefore, allowing one Louse, roughly, to each cubic millimetre, the population of the gall is about sixteen thousand. As I cannot count, I gauge. Even so did Herschel7 gauge the Milky Way. For numerical infinity, the Louse vies with the star. In four months the black atom, the first pioneer of the gall, has left all these descendants; and the end is not yet.

1 1⁄25 inch.—*Translator's Note.*

2 A little more than ¾ inch.—*B.M.*

3 The Abbé Charles François Lhomond (1727–1794), a famous French grammarian and classicist.—*Translator's Note.*

4 Not quite ¾ inch.—*Translator's Note.*

5 2.18 inch.—*Translator's Note.*

6 10 cubic inches.—*Translator's Note.*

7 Sir William Herschel (1738–1822), the Hanoverian-English astronomer, invented the principle of "gauging" the skies which was subsequently applied to the Milky Way by his son, Sir John Frederick William Herschel (1792–1871).—*Translator's Note.*

CHAPTER IV
THE TEREBINTH-LOUSE: THE MIGRATION

By the end of September the horn-shaped gall is full, almost as full as a keg of anchovies. There would not be room for them all were the Lice to form only one layer, side by side, with their suckers implanted. They lie in strata according to the length of their probe: uppermost are the big Lice, in the second layer the medium-sized and between their legs the small ones, all of them motionless, with their trunks at work. Above those engaged in drinking is the shifting horde, seeking a place at the refreshment bar. Eddies occur in the crowd: those at the top dive down, those underneath return to the surface; and this continual ebb and flow gives each one time for a little tippling.

In this rough and tumble the white waxen finery turns to flour, which fills up the interstices and makes of the whole a swarming conglomerate in which the metamorphosis is effected. Here, without a moment's quiet, the moult takes place and not a leg is out of joint: here, when there is no free space, wide wings are unfurled and not a wing is torn. To achieve transfiguration without a hitch in such a tumult the insect must be peculiarly favoured by fortune.

The pot-bellied orange Lice are now handsome, black, slender midges, provided with four wings. Their secluded life is over; the time has come for soaring in the open air. But how will they get out? The internees are quite incapable of making a breach in the ramparts: they have no tools. Well, what the prisoners cannot accomplish the fortress itself will do. When the population is ripe the gall is ripe too, so closely does the calendar of the bush synchronize with that of the insect.

The hems raise their upper folds a little; the spindles open like so many purses, each lined with pink satin; the auricles part their thick gnarled lips. The doors open of themselves for the impatient inmates, by the mere action of the sap. In the other galls, the globular and horn-shaped ones, the mechanism does not work so easily; the unclosing is a violent affair. More and more distended day by day, the globes burst their sides in star-shaped rents, while the horns split open at the top.

The exodus is worth close observation. I choose a few of the horn-shaped galls whose cracked tips announces the coming rupture. I expose them to the sun, in my study, facing a window, at a distance of a few paces from the closed casements. In the intervening space I set up a thick branch of leafy terebinth. I reckon upon this bait to attract the flying Lice, at least as a resting-spot. Next morning one of the horns opens, and by midday, in radiant sunlight, in calm, hot weather, the winged Lice are emerging.

They come forth in small companies, without hurrying. It is a quiet, gently-flowing stream. They are dusted over with a waxy flour, all that remains of the sometime powder-puffs. When barely on the threshold of the cranny, they spread their wings and are off, shedding a faint trail of dust from their shoulders, shaken by the vibrations of their wings. With an undulating flight they all make straight for the window, where the light is brighter than elsewhere. They dash against the panes and slip down upon the cross-bars. There, bathed in the sunlight, without attempting to go further afield, they remain, collecting in a drift.

Although the rest of the room is thoroughly well lit in all directions, the flight of the departing Lice is always directed towards the window facing the sun. There are thousands upon thousands of them; and not one takes another path, veering ever so little to the right or left. You feel a certain surprise at the invariable route pursued by these atoms which, when released, in a space well lit on every side, all, from the first to the last, rush towards the delights of a ray of sunshine. A handful of shot dropped from a height does not return to earth with greater certainty. The leaden pellets are attracted by gravity, to which all dead matter is subject, while the specks of living matter obey the light.

My window-panes check them. In the absence of this obstacle, where would they go? Certainly not to the terebinth-trees near by. I have definite proof of this here, before my eyes. As a resting-place I have set up a bough of the cherished bush. None of the newly emerged insects takes notice of it; none of them pauses there. If on the way to the window one of them collides with the green thicket and falls upon a leaf, it quickly picks itself up again and makes off in a hurry to join the others in the sunlit window. Freed henceforth from the demands of the stomach, they are no longer interested in the terebinth; they all avoid it.

The exodus lasts a couple of days. When the last loiterers have gone, let us open the gall entirely. The population has been rigorously sorted. At first it was a mixture of wingless red and winged black Lice. The latter have all left their dwelling; the others are still there. Those faithful to their home are small as before, squat, wrinkled and vermilion. Some of them bear the dorsal wallet, the maternal pouch. In them I recognize the legion of the mothers, now left alone in the house. For some time yet they linger on languidly, the gall being open to wind and weather; those less exhausted continue to produce offspring; mere abortions without a future; the time is too short and the house is falling into decay. At length they perish, with their belated young. The gall is a deserted ruin.

Let us return to the emigrants, checked in their flight by the window-panes. In shape, colour and size they are all alike; the swarm is a monotonous repetition of the same individual; there is not one detail, however minute, to denote any difference. Yet we should expect to find males and females here. The Plant-louse, until this moment in the humble larval stage, has just acquired the attributes of the perfect insect. The heavy, pot-bellied Louse has become a slender midge, glorified by four iridescent wings. In any other insect this would be an infallible token of the nuptial frolics.

Well, in the children of the galls, these wings, these adornments of maturity, belie their promises. There is no wedding and there can be none. Not a Louse in all the swarm is endowed with sex, and yet each has her brood, which she brings into the world by direct reproduction as her predecessors did.

With a slip of straw moistened with saliva I pick up a winged Louse at random. I press its abdomen with a pin. My brutal obstetrics produces an immediate effect: the insect's outraged flanks eject a string of five or six fœtuses; and the process is repeated without variation no matter what specimen we deliver.

Let us, for that matter, consult the natural procedure. A couple of hours elapse and my prisoners behind the window are in the throes of childbirth on the glass of the panes, the plaster of the embrasure, the wood of the cross-bars. Matters become so urgent that any place suits them.

The Louse in the act of parturition raises her two large wings, the upper pair, and gently moves the two small ones, the lower pair. The tip of the abdomen bends downwards, touches the supporting surface and the thing is done: a fœtus is implanted perpendicularly to the support, with its head uppermost. A little farther away, a second is deposited as promptly, followed by another and yet others. In one brief sitting the distribution is over. The average number of the litter is six.

The infant, we were saying, is fixed in an upright position, at right angles to the supporting surface. This nicely-balanced attitude is necessary. The new-born Louse is, in fact, wrapped in a thin tunic of which it must first of all divest itself. In a minute or two this swaddling band splits and is thrust backwards. The legs release themselves, kicking freely in all directions, which they could not do were the tiny creature lying on the ground. By this means joints that are working for the first time gain strength and suppleness. After a few moments of these gymnastic exercises, the tiny insect drops on its feet and wanders forth into the wide world.

While it is struggling in an upright position, passers-by sometimes knock it over, without consideration for its tender age. Then the danger is great. Thrown from its sticky pedestal, the little insect often perishes, incapable of casting off its slough. There are a few threads of cobweb in the corner of the window. Some winged Lice have been caught in them. The garlands of hanging Lice give birth to their offspring all the same, but the young ones, falling on the sill of the embrasure, cannot manage to strip, because they are not in a standing position.

Soon the cross-bars of the window are peopled with vermin, jogging along with great activity, promiscuously with the winged Lice. What a to-do on the borderland of the invisible! What are they seeking, these busy atoms? What do they want? My ignorance will be their undoing. In two or three days the winged Lice die. Their part is played. That of the children is beginning. For some time yet the latter wander about, but at last nothing stirs at the window; the legion of Lice is dead. Before sweeping them away with a camel's-hair brush, let us give a brief description of them. The new-born insects are pale green and slender in shape. Their length is not far short of a millimetre.1 Nimble and standing fairly high on their legs, they trot about busily.

The globular galls burst and the hems, auricles and spindles begin to gape a little earlier than the horn-shaped galls, about the middle of September. The five gall-makers of the terebinth all have the same customs. After emerging from their open dwellings, all the adults, or winged black Lice, give birth, within twenty-four hours, to a small number of young, some five or six, as do those of the horn-shaped galls.

The auricles yield a dumpy Louse, wider behind than before and of a dark olive colour. Her most remarkable feature is her sucker, which, folded underneath the insect, sticks out behind, recalling after a fashion a Grasshopper's oviscapt. What can the puny creatures want with this mechanism? It is a sword, a sabre. Held erect, the implement would prevent any attempt at walking. To drive it into the food-plant, the insect apparently hoists itself on its legs, which correspond in length with the enormous probe. I should like to see this inordinate beak at work. My captives refuse what I give them: leaves and fresh galls. They lie huddled on the plug of cotton-wool which closes the tube. They have business to attend to. They want to get away; but to what?

Likewise squat of build, packed, not without a certain prettiness, into the shape of miniature Toads, the Lice from the globular galls are a pale yellowish brown, while those of the folded leaves are greenish black. Neither the first nor the second have beaks of exaggerated length. That extraordinary rostrum, which sticks out behind, and, when at rest, resembles a caudal appendage, recurs in the young Lice from the spindle-shaped galls; but this time the little creature is oblong and its colour is pale green.

Let us cut short these dry details. It is enough if we recognize that these five fellow-guests of the terebinth are not of one race following different trades, but separate species. If the earlier generations, which all resemble one another, seemed to bear witness to a specific unity, the family of the winged Lice testifies to the contrary. These thickset insects and these slender ones; these bearers of the rostrum, sometimes of normal length and sometimes fantastically prolonged into the semblance of a caudal beak; these pale-green, olive-green, light-yellow insects are obviously independent forms.

A meticulous examination might find here preeminently all the characteristic features of the five categories; but the reader, repelled by prose descriptions, would soon turn the page. Let us pass on. Let us leave the insect laboratory, with its jars and test-tubes; let us go out of doors to see how matters come to pass under natural conditions on the terebinth in the grounds.

The galls, frequently inspected during the hottest hours of the day, open before my eyes; the horns are splitting at the top, the globes are opening their sides, the others are parting their lips. The moment the fissure is wide enough the black emigrants appear, without haste, one by one, in absolute composure, despite the fierceness of the sun. The exodus was not accomplished with greater sobriety in the comparative darkness of my study. For a few seconds they linger in the breach; then, shedding a dusty trail from their floury backs, they spread their wings and are off. Their flight, favoured by the least breath of air, promptly carries them to a distance at which I soon lose sight of them.

As a rule the exodus is partial, being distributed over several days. When the whole swarm has disappeared there are still the wingless red Lice, the hump-backed pigmies, the progenitors of the big migrants. Some of them come to enjoy a little sunlight on the brink of the aperture. They soon go in again. Others follow them; perhaps they too are attracted by the brilliant sunshine. Then we see none at all. The festival of the light is not for them. For a week or two longer they lead a hand-to-mouth existence in the ruined gall, but their end is not far off. The withered gall starves them and old age kills them where they stand.

So far there is nothing new: my laboratory experiments have already shown me what the terebinth in the garden tells me. The window-panes and test-tubes have even taught me more than the tree: they have enabled me to realize the part played by the winged Lice. In the liberty of the open air one fundamental detail of their story escapes me, for parturition takes place at a distance, I do not know where. The new-born Lice must be scattered everywhere, often at a considerable distance, as the emigrant's flight informs me. Shall I then not find on the tree itself the little Lice with which my indoor observations have made me familiar? Yes: and in circumstances which are worth recording.

Let me recapitulate: to escape from their galls, strongly-built dungeons without any outlet, the Terebinth-Lice have no means of breaking through. Though very clever at tickling vegetable tissues and making them swell into excrescences, they can do nothing with the walls of their prison. When it is time to go, however impatient they may be to get out, they must wait until the gall opens of itself, until the horn, in particular, splits into jagged segments at the top and the globe bursts open at the side. Until the fort is thus spontaneously dismantled, there is no possibility of escape.

Now it may happen that the winged population is ripe and ready to increase and multiply before there is a breach in the wall, either because the gall is not yet sufficiently distended, or because it has dried up before its time and is henceforth unable to open.

What do the captives do in the event of such a disaster? Precisely what they would do in the open air. Their business cannot be postponed. When the imperious hour has struck they bring forth their young, one on top of another, in such a crush that it is hardly possible to move. For good, or ill, the great task is accomplished.

In this tangle of wings a-flutter in the midst of a waxy powder, this skirmish of legs seeking equilibrium on an ever-shifting support, many young Lice are trampled underfoot and injured, many are unable to strip and shrivel into grains of dust. The majority, none the less, so tenacious of life are they, contrive to escape in the swarming confusion.

Let us, in October, open a globular or horn-shaped gall which has dried up without bursting. We shall find it crammed with black Lice, all winged and all dead; a mass of procreators who have died after parturition. Beneath the heap of corpses, more especially against the walls of the dwelling, the lens, in amazement, discovers thousands of young ones. This is a new people: it is the future struggling amidst the cadaveric relics of the past; it is the progeny of the winged Lice, the family born in prison. Here and there, in the midst of this bustling youth, are vermilion-coloured specks, more awkward in their gait but as lively as the rest. These are the grandmothers of the colony, still doing fairly well and capable, I should say, of surviving the winter.

I have some hope of keeping them alive, they look so healthy. Perhaps their part is not yet fully played. I set them aside, together with their galls, opened with a penknife. If left to the inclemencies of the weather in their ruined cells, they would die when the cold sets in; but may they not hold out if sheltered under glass? I almost think they will.

And indeed at the outset things do not go so badly. My little red insects continue to look in the best of health. Then, at the first frosts, they become motionless, though still fresh in appearance as though they meant to return to life in the spring. Appearances deceive; the motionless Lice never move again. Long before April the whole herd is dead. My care has slightly delayed the dissolution, without preventing the inevitable end. None the less I marvel at the tenacious vitality of the little red grandmothers. They live half the year, their daughters but a few days.

Released henceforward from the necessity of feeding themselves, the black emigrants, the winged Lice, leave their terebinth and need not search for another, as is proved by my bough, which, placed in the path of the emerging insects, does not even serve them as a temporary resting-place. They seem equally heedless in selecting a spot for the establishment of their family. Before my window the young Lice are dropped at random, at any point to which the hazards of flight have led: on the window-panes, the plaster of the embrasure, the wood of the cross-bars or the threads of cobweb indifferently. There is nothing to show that the unfamiliar spot is regarded as inopportune. There is no sign of uneasiness, no attempt to fly off elsewhither, to a more propitious place. Soberly and serenely, the winged legion brings forth its young and goes its way.

In the open country things must happen no otherwise. The moment they are free, the emigrants shake off their waxen dust and flit away in this direction or in that, according to the prevailing breeze. A flying-machine has sprouted from their shoulders, a remarkable contrast to the clumsy paunch of their early days. Quick, for the sunlight, for flight, for the joys of the ballet in mid-air! Off they go, hovering as long as their feeble wings allow; then, wearied of merry-making in the sun, they alight on the first object that offers, without henceforth renewing their flight as do my prisoners behind the closed window. Here, no matter what the nature of the site, parturition takes place. There is nothing left for them but to die.

With these urgent methods, disdainful of deliberate selection, the wastage among the emigrants' tiny offspring must be great. On the bare soil, on stones, on dry bark, the little Lice undoubtedly perish. They need food quickly; and they are scarcely capable of wandering in quest of it themselves. Their sucker, sometimes of inordinate length, projecting beyond the tip of the abdomen like a caudal rapier, demands that the wearer shall erect it, shall drive it into some yielding source of sap. The insect must drink or die. In the test-tubes wherein I collect the young Lice born before my eyes, my captives die in less than a fortnight from want of food.

I try various kinds of green stuff. I have no success with any of them. But here, if direct observation fails me, logic comes to my assistance. There is no doubt that the tiny Lice, at the present moment the sole representatives of their race, must live through the winter and serve as the origin of the population which will occupy the terebinth in the spring. These puny creatures cannot remain exposed to the severities of the winter. A shelter is indispensable, a shelter that will afford them both food and lodging. Where will they find it? Only one shelter is possible: it must be underground, beneath some sort of grass that will retain a little green in winter.

It is, in fact, to be presumed that the thick tufts of certain grasses will afford them shelter. This abiding-place, where the sucker will sink into the sweet root-fibres, and where the drip of rain or snow does not easily find access, is beloved by several Plant-lice. Those of the terebinth also may very well take up their winter-quarters there. As for what happens in these subterranean lairs, we are reduced to more or less probable conjectures.

1 1/25 inch.—*Translator's Note.*

CHAPTER V
THE DORTHESIA

After the exodus of the young, when she deserts her tent of swansdown, half a finger's-breadth in thickness, very warm and soft, but blocked with rubbish which would hamper a second family, the Clotho Spider1 proceeds to fashion elsewhere a light hammock with a canopy, an inexpensive summer-house where she will pass the remainder of the warm weather. Those who are not yet marriageable ask no better protection against the inclemencies of the winter; their robust powers of endurance are satisfied with a muslin tent under the shelter of a stone.

The matrons, on the other hand, as the heat begins to decrease, hasten to enlarge and strengthen their cells, lavishing upon them the contents of their silk-reservoirs, which the hunting-expeditions of the fine summer nights have left distended. When the sharp white-frosts set in they will doubtless find more comfort in their luxurious mansions than in the first rickety hovels; nevertheless, they do not build them precisely for themselves but rather for the use of their expected offspring; wherefore the walls are never stout nor the feather-beds downy enough.

The superb structure of the Clotho is above all a nest, beside which those of the Chaffinch and the Siskin are but squatter's huts. The mother, it is true, does not sit upon her eggs, being as she is without an incubator; she does not feed her offspring, who for that matter do not require her assistance; but the part which she plays is, none the less, one of exquisite tenderness. For seven or eight months she watches over her brood, protecting it with a devotion equal to that of the bird, or even greater.

Maternity, the supreme inspiration of the noblest instincts, has thousands upon thousands of masterpieces to bear witness to its skill. Let us recall that of the Labyrinth Spider.2 What a wonderful achievement is the spacious building where the mother mounts guard about the star-shaped tabernacle, the family cradle! What an eminently logical stronghold is this rampart of silk reinforced by masonry, to protect the eggs from the probe of the Ichneumon-fly!

Similarly, each mother has her own defensive methods, which are sometimes the most ingenious inventions and sometimes devices of extreme simplicity. The strange thing is that the distribution of talents takes no account whatever of the insect hierarchy. Certain insects of the highest rank, protected by sumptuous wing-cases, or sporting lofty plumes, or attired in garments of imbricated gold scales, are almost or quite incapable of doing anything; they are magnificent duffers, whereas others, among the very humblest, and passing unperceived, amaze us by their talents when we grant them our attention.

But do not things happen likewise amongst ourselves? True merit shuns indolent luxury. If we are to turn to the best advantage the little good which may lie hidden within us, we must feel the incentive of need. As long as nineteen centuries ago, Persius prefaced his satires with the lines:

Magister artis ingenique largitor Venter.

One of our proverbs repeats his views in terms a little less crude:

L'homme est comme la nèfle; il n'est rien qui vaille

S'il n'amûri longtemps au grenier, sur la paille.[3]

Insects are like ourselves. Necessity stimulates their wits and at times enables them to make discoveries which upset all our conceptions. I know of one, amongst the humblest and least well-known, which, to safeguard its progeny, has found the following strange solution of the problem: at the laying-season, the normal length of the body is trebled: the fore part is left at the service of the insect, which feeds, digests, roams about and shares in the joys of the sunlight; and the hinder part becomes an infant's crêche, a nursery in which the little ones are gently exercised.

This singular creature is called the Dorthesia (*D. Characias*, Latt). We find it from time to time on the Greater Spurge, which the Greeks used to call *Characias* and which the Provençal peasant of to-day calls *Chusclo, Lachusclo.*

A lover of the climate in which the olive flourishes, this spurge abounds on the Sérignan hills, in the driest spots, where its great blue-green tufts contrast with the poverty-stricken vegetation of the neighbourhood. Standing in a bed of pebbles which reflect the sun's rays upon it, by its vigorous foliage it protests against the hardships of winter. Still, it is not devoid of prudence. When the foolish almond-tree is already abandoning its shivering petals to the north-east wind, the spurge, less hasty, continues to observe the weather and keeps the tender tips of its blossoms rolled up crosier-wise for protection. The worst frosts are over. Then, with a sudden urge of sap, the stems swell with a milk that burns like hot coals and the crosiers uncurl and straighten out into clusters of dingy little flowers, at which the first Gnats of the year come to slake their thirst.

Wait a few days longer. As the weather grows milder, we shall see a numerous population slowly emerging from the heap of leaves that have fallen at the foot of the spurge. It is the Dorthesia quitting her winter quarters under the remnants of the old foliage, and climbing, gradually, by cautious stages, from the base to the topmost summits of the plant, where the joys of heat and radiant light await her, together with the delights of an inexhaustible feeding-bottle.

In April, or at latest in May, the ascent is completed; all the little creatures are assembled on the topmost tips of the branches, in close-packed groups, side touching side, after the fashion of the Plant-lice. A sap-drinker and endowed with a beak that acts as a gimlet, the Dorthesia is, in fact, related to the Aphides, whose sedentary and social habits she shares; but, far from reminding us in appearance of the plump, naked vermin which the rose-tree and so many other plants have made familiar to us, she is clothed, and her costume is one of unusual elegance.

The orange Terebinth-lice, imprisoned in galls, whether horn-shaped or rounded like apricots, attach to their hinder parts a long train of extreme delicacy, which the slightest touch reduces to dust. In the Dorthesiæ, on the other hand, we see a complete garment, a close-fitting coat of indefinite length, though fragile and breaking off in particles under the point of a needle, just as a brittle rind might do.

Nothing could be prettier than the cloak of this large Louse, either in shape or in colour. It is a uniform dead white, more pleasing to the eye than even the white of milk. The forepart of the garment is a jacket of curly knots arranged in four longitudinal rows between which other, smaller knots are distributed. The hinder part is a fringe of ten slats gradually increasing in width and spreading outwards, not unlike the teeth of a comb. The breast is covered by a shirt-front formed of symmetrical plates and pierced with six neatly-rounded holes, through which the brown legs emerge, quite naked and unconstrained. This shirt-front and the curly mantle on the back together form a sort of sleeveless woollen waistcoat with easy-fitting armholes. In the same way the hood is pierced by holes to give free play to the rostrum and the antennæ. All the other parts are covered by the white cloak.

This is the winter costume; it covers the whole body but does not extend beyond it. Later, when the laying-season draws near, the garment grows longer, as though the insect, which in reality cannot undergo further change, were growing at a furious rate and trebling its length. Gracefully curved like the prow of a gondola, the new portion is furrowed above by wide parallel grooves; underneath it is finely streaked, almost smooth. The end is cut off square. The magnifying-glass here reveals a transverse button-hole plugged with fine cotton-wool.

The material of the garment is everywhere brittle, fusible and inflammable; when laid on paper it leaves a slightly translucent mark. From these qualities we judge it to be a sort of wax, similar to beeswax. In order to obtain it in some other form than that of tiny particles removed from the insect, I collect a handful of Dorthesiæ and subject them to the action of boiling water. The waxen coverings melt and dissolve into an oily liquid which floats on the surface; the denuded insects sink to the bottom. On cooling, the thin floating layer sets into an amber-yellow sheet.

This colour causes us a certain surprise. We began with a substance whose whiteness rivalled that of milk; and now melting gives it a look of resin. This is a matter of molecular arrangement and nothing more. To impart a proper whiteness to the yellow wax as it comes from the hive, the wax-chandler melts it down and pours the melted substance into cold water, thereby reducing it to thin flakes which he afterwards exposes, on wattled screens, to the rays of the sun. Further meltings follow, with a further production of shell-like flakes and further exposure to the bright sunshine; and, little by little, the wax turns white by changing its molecular structure. In this art of bleaching how far our superior is the Dorthesia! Without treating the material by repeated meltings and prolonged exposures to the sun, she then and there transforms a yellow wax into one of incomparable whiteness. She obtains by her gentle methods a result that eludes the violent procedures of the laboratory.

Like beeswax, the Dorthesia's wax is not collected in the outer world: it is a first product, exuded through the surface of the body. No manipulation is required to induce it to form itself into curly knots, to fall into uniform streaks or graceful flutings. Merely in exuding from the pores of the skin, it automatically acquires the requisite form; like the fledgling's plumage, its clothing grows correctly by the mere activities of the organism; the wearer of the dress has no need to improve upon it.

The tiny creature, when it issues from the egg, is perfectly naked, and brown in colour. Soon, before leaving the mother and settling on the bark of the spurge to draw its first sips, it becomes covered with thinly-scattered white specks, which form the first outline of the future jacket. By slow degrees these specks increase in number and are produced into curly knots, so much so that the youngster, at the moment of its emancipation, is clad like its elders.

The exudation of the wax is continuous; the white tunic is constantly growing larger and nearer to perfection. Therefore the insect, if I cunningly strip it bare, ought to be capable of clothing itself anew. Experiment confirms my expectations. Destroying her garments with the point of a needle and brushing them off with a camel-hair pencil, I completely denude a mature Dorthesia. The persecuted Louse comes forth in her poor brown skin. I isolate her on a sprig of spurge. In two or three weeks' time the coat has been remade; not so full as the first, but large enough and of the regulation cut. With the wax which would have added to the original garment the insect has sweated forth another.

What is the use of this backward prolongation which trebles the actual size of the body? Is it merely an adornment? It is much more than that.

Let us, once April is here, detach and lay open this strange appendage. It is hollow, and full of an incomparable downy wadding; no feather-bed or eider-down could boast of so fine, so white a filling. In the midst of this magnificent eider-down some ovoid beads are scattered, some white and others tinged with a ruddy brown. These are the eggs. The new-born insects are swarming amongst them, higgledy-piggledy; some are bare and brown, some are more or less speckled with white, according to the more or less advanced state of the coat.

On the other hand, let us watch the Dorthesia idly roaming about the spurge. At long intervals we shall see emerging from the orifice at the end of the padded pocket a young Louse, handsomely clad, and nimble in his movements, who chooses his place beside his mother and settles down, plunging his bill into the juicy bark. He will not stir again until the well is dry. Others follow him from day to day; and this goes on for months on end!

If we were guided only by these observations we should conclude that the mother was viviparous, given to dropping, here and there, living offspring, all ready dressed. Nothing of the kind: we have just found in the thickly-quilted pocket both eggs and young. Moreover, the laying and hatching of the eggs may be witnessed without difficulty.

In a glass tube provided with a sprig of spurge I segregate a few mothers whose terminal wallet I have removed. Laid bare, the insect's hind-quarters have no further secrets from us; I see, sprouting from them, a sort of white mildew, like an unshaven beard. This is the waxy secretion that sprouts from the insect's hind-quarters, producing, instead of tassels, filaments of extreme fineness. It is thus that the down which fills the wallet must be produced. Presently, in the midst of this tuft of down, an egg appears, like those which we obtained by breaking into the maternal treasury.

This method enables me to estimate the size of the clutch. Two Dorthesiæ stripped bare behind and isolated, with provisions, in a glass tube, produced, in thirteen days, thirty eggs, or fifteen apiece, or rather more than one egg daily. As the process of laying continues for nearly five months, the total number of eggs for a single mother must be nearly two hundred.

The eggs hatch in three or four weeks' time. The hatching is announced by a change in the colour of the egg, which from white becomes a bright reddish-brown. On leaving the egg-shell the infant Louse is reddish-brown and absolutely naked. Its appearance is that of a very tiny Spider, the more so as its long antennæ look very like a fourth pair of legs. Before long, four longitudinal rows of tiny white tufts appear on its back, with bare spaces between them. This is the beginning of the waxen mantle.

The protracted period of egg-laying, which continues for four months or more, the comparatively quick hatching, and, finally, the gradual exudation of the Louse's clothing, explain why white eggs and reddish-brown eggs, with naked youngsters and others more or less clothed, are found simultaneously in the maternal pouch. This pouch is a warehouse in which the Louse's eggs are collected for months together.

Inside the pouch, in the depths of its luxurious padding, the young Lice are born, grow up, and clothe themselves in wax before risking the dangers of the open. The mother gently carries them from twig to twig of the spurge without troubling herself as to those that emerge from her pouch. One by one, as they feel themselves strong enough, they migrate, when their time has come, to settle down in the neighbourhood. The exit from their home is always open; they have only to force their way through the barrier of down.

The Narbonne Lycosa carries her family about with much less tenderness and security. There is no shelter on the back of the Gipsy Spider, no safeguard against falls, which are frequent in such a scramble. The Dorthesia, more happily inspired, makes a box of the skirts of her mantle and a downy bed of her caudal tufts. To find an equivalent method we must go back from the Spurge-louse to the first-born of the Mammifers—Kangaroos, Opossums and others—who rear their young in a pouch formed by a fold of the skin of the abdomen. Coming before its time, the shapeless embryo fixes itself on the teat and completes its development in the maternal pouch or *marsupium*.

Let us make use of this term to denote the Dorthesia's pouch. There is a great similarity between the two wallets, although the insect is superior to the mammal in this respect: Life often begins with excellence in the lowly and ends with mediocrity in the strong. In the original device of the *marsupium* a Louse has done better than the Opossum.

With the object of following the history of my insects more conveniently than was possible under the blaze of the sun by the roadside, I placed before one of my study windows a fine clump of spurge transplanted into a capacious flowerpot. As a result of my diligence the plant was populated during the course of March by three or four dozen Dorthesiæ, all wearing more or less fully developed *marsupia*. My experiment in the domestication of plant and insect was extremely successful: the spurge did well, so its inhabitants prospered also.

The wallets became filled with eggs and then with young Lice, who, matured in the nick of time, and more numerous every day, emerged and spread themselves at will over the spurge. During the heat of the summer you might have thought it had snowed on the plant, so populous was the colony of white Lice. It contained thousands of new inhabitants, varying in size and easily distinguished from the mothers and foundresses by their smaller dimensions, but above all by the complete absence of the *marsupium*, an addition which must develop very much later, after hibernation at the root of the food-plant.

Some are larger and others smaller, according to age, for the matrons still continue to procreate, but all wear the same costume and present the same appearance; yet certain differences, unnoticed at the time of my summary examination, should divide them into two groups, one very small, consisting almost wholly of exceptions, and the other forming the vast majority.

In August these differences become very plainly visible. On the tips of the leaves, here and there, are isolated a few Lice who are surrounding themselves with a fragile waxen enclosure, a sort of shapeless capsule, while the rest of the flock, nearly all, in fact, continue to drink, their bills plunged into the bark. Who are these solitaries, withdrawn from the world of drinkers? They are males, undergoing transformation. I open some of these fragile capsules. In the centre, on a downy bed like that which fills the wallets of the mothers, lies a nymph endowed with wing-stumps. At the beginning of September I obtain the first males in their perfect state.

Strange creatures, in truth! Standing high on their legs, with long horns, they have the look of certain Bugs. The body is black and powdered with a fine waxy powder, the remains of the capsule in which the transformation took place. The wings are of a leaden grey, rounded at the tips, overlapping one another when at rest and protruding a long way beyond the extremity of the abdomen. To the rear is an aigrette of white filaments, very long and straight, composed, no doubt, of wax, like the cloak of the larval stage. It is a very fragile ornament: the insect loses most of it merely in wandering about among the few leaves in his glass prison, the tube in which I am observing him.

In moments of elation the tip of the abdomen rises between the lifted wings and the bundle of spokes spreads out fanwise. The insect is showing off, erecting his tail, like the peacock. To glorify his nuptials, he has attached a comet's tail to his rump; he displays it fanwise, closes it, opens it again, making it quiver and glisten in the sunlight. When the crisis of joy has passed his finery is folded up and the abdomen sinks down under cover of the wings.

The head is small, with long antennæ. At the tip of the abdomen is a short, pointed projection, a sort of hook, an implement of pairing. Of mouth-parts or rostrum there is absolutely not a trace. What would he do with them, this microcephalous coxcomb? He has changed his shape only to flirt for a moment with his neighbours of the other sex, to mate and to die. Moreover, the part which he fulfils does not seem to be particularly necessary. On the spurge in my study the female population of the second generation numbers several thousands, and I obtain, in all, some thirty males. Approximately, there are a hundred times as many females. The dandified wearers of the aigrette cannot suffice for such a harem.

On the other hand, they do not seem to be very eager. I see some who, on emerging from the ruins of their capsule, covered with powder, brush and wipe themselves a little, try their wings, and then, with a lazy flight, make for the window, which is closed to prevent their escape. The festival of the sunlight is to them a greater attraction than the emotions of pairing. It is possible that the indifferent lighting of the room is in this case the cause of their coldness. In the open country, under the direct rays of the sun, they would certainly have displayed their finery amidst the marriageable females, and the business of pairing would not have lacked ardour. But even though the most favourable circumstances had conditioned the pairing, the exaggerated number of females, out of all proportion to the males, tells us that very few are chosen among many that are called: roughly about one in a hundred. Nevertheless, all produce offspring. With these singular creatures it is enough that a few mothers are fecundated from time to time, and the race continues to thrive. The impulse communicated to the elect is a heritage which is handed down for some considerable time, on condition that a few couples, year by year, restore to the community its exhausted energies.

A parasite frequently observed in Bee-hives, the *Monodontomerus,* has already shown us a similar example of the rarity of the males. Two tiny little creatures tell us of a vast field yet to be tilled by our genetic theories. One day, perhaps, they will help us to unravel the obscure problem of the sexes.

Meanwhile the old mothers, the Dorthesiæ bearing the *marsupium,* grow day by day fewer on the spurge. Their ovaries exhausted and their wallets empty, they fall to the ground, where the Ants cut them to pieces. On the plant only those young mothers whose maternal pouches will not begin to make an appearance until the return of spring are visible nearly till Christmas. When the cold becomes severe the flock descends to the foot of the spurge, under the heap of dead leaves. They will come up again at the end of March, slowly climbing the spurge-plant, to acquire the rearing-pouch and begin once again the cycle of evolution.

1 Cf. *The Life of the Spider*: chap. xvi.—*Translator's Note.*

2 Cf. *The Life of the Spider*: chap. xv.—*Translator's Note.*

3 Man is like the medlar: he is worth nothing
Unless he has ripened long in the granary, on the straw.

CHAPTER VI
THE KERMES OF THE OAK1

The nest, that notable expression of maternal skill and care, is rivalled by other modes of rearing which often reveal the most wonderful tenderness. The Lycosa drags behind her, hanging to her spinnerets, the wallet of eggs that bangs against her legs; and for half the year she carries about on her back her young, fore-gathered in a serried group. In like fashion does the Scorpion nurse her offspring on her back; for a fortnight she allows them to gather strength against the moment of emancipation. Exuding a white wax, the Dorthesia contrives at the tip of the abdomen an exquisite muff into which the young are born, and in which they adorn themselves with cottony tufts and peacefully grow ripe for the exodus. The downy refuge, with its narrow opening, allows the secluded offspring to emerge, one by one, as they become capable of settling down upon the fostering spurge.

Lowly among the lowliest, the Kermes of the oak has invented something even better: the mother, transformed into an unassailable fortress, bequeaths to her family, as its cradle, her skin, toughened into an ebony bastion.

In May let us patiently examine, in sunny corners, the slender twigs of the holm-oak or evergreen oak. Let us also inspect that cross-grained shrub with small prickly leaves, known to the Provençal peasant as the *avaus*, and to botanists as the kermes oak. This wretched brushwood, which one can pass over in a single stride, is really an oak, a genuine oak, as is proved by its handsome acorns, set in their rough, prickly cups. We will gather our harvest here as well as on the holm-oak. But we shall pass by the ordinary or English oak; we should find on it nothing in the least like what we are seeking to-day. Only the two species first mentioned will repay exploration.

On these we shall see, a few here and a few there, but never in abundance, certain globules of a glossy black, about the bigness of a moderate-sized pea. Here we have the Kermes, one of the strangest of insects. But is this an insect? Is it of the animal kingdom? The uninitiated would never suspect such a thing; he would take the object for a berry, some species of black current. The mistake is all the more natural in that the globule, if bitten into, cracks, and yields a sweetish flavour, offset by a slight bitterness.

And this all but delicious fruit, we are told, is of the animal kingdom; it is an insect. Let us look at the creature closely, through the pocket microscope. We look for a head, an abdomen, and legs. There is absolutely not a vestige of a head, nor of an abdomen, nor of legs; all there is to be seen is a sort of large bead, fit for that cheap jewellery which is made of jet. Is there not at least that division into segments, which is the documentary proof of the insect? No! A pebble is not more lifeless.

Perhaps we shall find on the under surface of the globule, in the part in contact with the twig, some trace of animal structure? The bead comes away easily and without breaking, like a berry. The base is slightly flattened and powdered with a white waxy substance which acts as a cement and causes the bead to adhere to the twig. Soaked in alcohol for twenty-four hours this substance dissolves and leaves uncovered the part to be examined.

Careful examination with the lens fails to reveal on the base of the bead the legs, or claws, however minute, which would serve to establish the fact of animal life. Nor does it reveal the sucker which, implanted in the bark, would imbibe the sap, that indispensable aliment. Although less smooth than the back, this portion is as bare as the rest. One would say, in fact, that the Kermes adheres to the twig because it is cemented to it, but has no other connection with it.

This cannot be the case. The black bead feeds itself; it grows; and without cessation it pours forth a product which might be the work of the distiller. To make up for such expenditure it must at least possess a rostrum to perforate the juicy bark. It assuredly does possess such an organ, but so small that my worn eyes are powerless to detect it.

At the very moment of detaching the Kermes from its support the implement of suction may possibly withdraw itself, shrinking into itself to the point of becoming invisible.

In that half of the sphere which lies toward the base of the twig, the globule is traversed by a wide furrow which occupies the greater part of the half-meridian. At the lower edge of this furrow, on the confines of the supporting base, is a narrow opening, in the shape of a button-hole. By this opening only is the Kermes in touch with the outer world. It is a gate which serves many functions, and first of all, that of a fountain of syrup.

Let us cull a few twigs of evergreen oak peopled by Kermes and place the cut ends in a glass of water. The foliage will remain fresh for some time—a condition which will suffice to ensure the insects' welfare. We shall see, ere long, a colourless, transparent fluid which, in the course of a couple of days, collects itself into a drop equal in volume to the flask from which it oozes. If it becomes too heavy the drop falls, but without flowing over the Kermes, for the outlet is as it were a postern gate. Another drop at once begins to form. The spring is not intermittent, but perpetual; uninterrupted it sheds its solitary tears.

With the tip of the little finger let us gather this drop from the still and taste it. Delicious! In taste and aroma it is very nearly equal to honey. If the Kermes were to lend itself to wholesale rearing as well as to the easy harvesting of its product, we should have in it a valuable sugar-refiner. But it is for others to exploit it with the needful diligence and devotion.

These others are the Ants, those patient harvesters. They make for the Kermes even more eagerly than for the Plant-louse or Green-fly. The latter is niggardly in the matter of yielding its ambrosia; the Ant has to solicit it with patience; tickling its paunch before she can obtain even a meagre sip from the tips of its tiny horns. The Kermes is a spendthrift. Fully consenting, and at any moment, it permits all comers to quench their thirst from its cellar, and its liquid *largesse* is offered in streams.

The Ants, therefore, crowd about the distillery; they form quite a company; by threes and fours they lick the opening of the gourd-like vessel; and however high the Kermes is installed amidst the foliage of the oak, they possess a most wonderful power of discovering it. When I see one slowly climbing I have only to follow her with my eyes; she takes me straight to the Ant's tavern. She is my infallible guide when, still in its early youth, the Kermes by its minuteness would escape the glance of an eye not warned and on the alert. Even the very tiny insects are perambulating taverns and are well frequented like the big ones.

On the tree, in the full liberty of the fields, the diligence of the Ants, collecting the syrup as it oozes forth, will hardly permit us to estimate the value of the spring. The little round barrel, incessantly drained dry, shows barely a trace of moisture round the bung-hole. We must take an isolated twig, far from thirsty drinkers, to determine the true value of this flask of nectar. Then, in the absence of the Ants, we see the liquor collecting with considerable rapidity in a drop of surprising volume. The extravasated fluid exceeds the capacity of the beaker, and the trickling continues, as evenly and abundantly as before. The sugar-refinery is now in permanent business; when there is no syrup left there is still plenty to come.

The Ants rear the Plant-lice, their milch-cows. What herds they would amass, what incalculable benefits they would derive therefrom, if the Kermes could only be reared in captivity! But it is found only in isolated groups, which, for that matter, are not numerous in themselves, and it cannot be moved from spot to spot. Removed from its position it dies, unable to take root elsewhere. The Ants exploit it where they find it, without the slightest effort to gather together a flock of Lice in a leafy chalet. Their ingenuity wisely draws back when confronted by the impossible.

What is the purpose of this nectar, so plentiful and so highly appreciated by the connoisseur? Can it be that it flows forth for the benefit of the Ants? After all, why not? In virtue of their number and their activity as harvesters, they perform a function of far-reaching significance in the general picnic of living creatures. As the price of their services, they are granted the horn-shaped nectar of the Plant-louse and the fountain of the Kermes.

At the end of May let us break open the black capsule. Beneath the envelope, hard and brittle, a hasty dissection shows us eggs: nothing but eggs. We looked for the apparatus of a distiller of liqueurs, for rows of retorts; we find only an obtrusive ovary. The Kermes is little more than a coffer bursting with germs.

The germs are white, and assembled to the number of thirty or thereabouts, in little groups or clusters, which remind us, as regards their arrangement, of the masses of seeds in the buttercup. Tufts of extremely fine tracheal filaments encompass the glomeruli, surrounding them with an inextricable litter which makes an exact count impossible. A rough approximation gives us a hundred. The total of the eggs would therefore be some thousands.

What does the Kermes want with this prodigious number of offspring? An alchemist of the general food supply, it does as do so many others among the humble creatures predestined to the elaboration of nutritive molecules: by means of excess numbers it seeks to avert the extermination with which it is threatened. With its liquor it provides the Ant, an importunate guest perhaps, but not a dangerous one, with a delicious beverage; on the other hand, with its eggs it nourishes a consumer who would lead to the extinction of the Kermes, were it not itself subjected to a drastic thinning out.

It has so happened that I have found the lover of omelettes at work. It is a negligible little grub which creeps from one tiny cluster to another, emptying his eggs still enclosed in their natal sheath. As a usual thing it is alone; sometimes it has companions—two, three or more. Ten, according to my notes, is the largest number recorded by its holes of exit.

How did it find its way into the strong-box, armoured on every side with impenetrable horn? We may be sure that it was introduced while yet a germ through the button-hole aperture whence oozes the syrup. A mother must have chanced this way, who, discovering the orifice, took a sip, and then, turning herself about, plunged her oviduct into the opening. Here, without use of violence, the enemy entered the citadel.

The enemy belongs to the tribe of Chalcidians, those zealous ransackers of entrails. An extremely rapid worker, she acquires her adult form and emerges from the shell in the early part of June. In comparison with the offspring of the Kermes she is a giant, being no less than a twelfth part of an inch in length. The narrow dormer-window by which the germ was introduced being no longer able to give it passage, the recluse, with his patient, steely tooth, opens a door of emergence for himself through the wall of the shell, so that the latter is finally pierced with as many round openings as there were fellow-feasters. When they have departed the coffer is empty; there is no trace left of the plentiful omelette.

This ravager of ovaries is of a deep bluish-black colour; dark, concave wings, closely pressed down after the fashion of the elytral apron, giving it a vague look of the Beetle family. The head is flattened, projecting beyond the corselet on either side; the powerful mandibles are such as are needed to perforate the tough, leathery wall. The long antennæ, incessantly vibrating, bent at an angle, slightly dilated at the tip, are ornamented with a white ring. Dumpy and thickset, the tiny creature runs swiftly along, polishing its wings and brushing its antennæ; it is full of delight at having emptied the belly of a Kermes. Has it a name in our scientific catalogue? I do not know, and am not especially anxious to know. A label in barbarous Latin would afford the reader no more information than would a few lines of history.

June is nearly over. For some time the sugary oozing has ceased; the Ants no longer come to their restaurant, a sign of profound alteration within. The outer aspect, however, has undergone no modification. We still have the small, black, glossy sphere, smooth and firmly fixed on its base, which is whitened with wax. With the point of a pen-knife let us break open the ebony casket, at the upper pole, at a point opposite the point of adhesion. Its wall is quite as hard and brittle as the wing-cover of a Scarabæus. Within, not a trace remains of the juicy pulp: the contents consist of a dry meal, a mixture of red and white specks.

Let us collect this powder in a small glass tube; let us reinforce our sight by a magnifying-glass, and examine it. The appearance of the stuff is amazing. This dust is moving, these ashes are alive, and with life so numerous that the very idea of computation becomes alarming. It is the legion of the uncountable. In safeguarding a Louse fecundity knows no limits.

By their white hue we may distinguish those eggs that are not yet ripe for hatching. Now, at the end of June, these are the less numerous. The others, coloured by the tiny creatures within them, are bright red or orange yellow. Preponderant over all is the collection of white specks, the tattered husks of the eggs which have been hatched.

Now these discarded husks are arranged in radiating clusters, just as were the germs in the glomerulus of the ovary. This detail informs us that there was no period of egg-laying; that is, not only were the eggs not conveyed to a point external to the mother's body, but they were not even conveyed to any particular point of the enclosure bounded by the carapace, by a common protecting roof. They were hatched on the very site of their formation. The bunches of eggs, their arrangement and position remaining unchanged, have become clusters of offspring.

The Psyche has already provided an example of that singular genesis which exempts the mother from the process of egg-laying, the family being hatched out on the spot occupied by the eggs. Let us recall the shapeless moth, whose appearance is even more miserable than that of the caterpillar. She withdraws herself into the husk of her chrysalid, and there she wastes away, swollen with eggs which will be hatched on the spot. The mother Psyche becomes a lifeless bag whence emerges her living family. This is likewise the case of the Kermes.

I witness the process of birth. The new-born insects are struggling to escape from their envelopes. Many of them succeed in doing so by leaving the delicate husk of the egg where it is fastened, still included in the radiating pattern. Others, no less numerous, drag their sheath from its place and for a long time trail it after them, hanging to their hinder parts. It adheres so firmly that the tiny creature is able to cross the threshold of the shell with its moulted husk, completing its liberation in the open air. Thus it is that we find on the natal twig, at some distance from the maternal pill, numbers of white discarded husks, which, if one had not closely followed the progress of events, would give one reason to believe that the eggs were hatched outside the Kermes. These filmy envelopes are deceptive; for the whole family was hatched inside the coffer.

Having collected the living dust with which it is now filled, let us glance at the ebony box itself. The cavity is divided into two storeys by a transverse partition, a fine-spun relic of the dessicated animal. The individual substance of the Kermes was so little that it is now represented by a delicate film. The rest of the mass enclosed by the shell appertains to the ovaries. The upper storey is therefore occupied by the newly born no less than the lower.

It is easy to emerge from this latter compartment when the time of the exodus has arrived; at its base is an ever-open door, a fissure shaped like a button-hole. But how is it possible to escape from the upper storey, separated from the other as it is by a partition? The newly-hatched young are so feeble, so tiny, that they would never be able to break through the membrane. Let us look more closely. The partition is pierced in the centre by a round manhole! The inhabitants of the lower storey can make immediate use of the door of their dwelling-house, the button-hole exit; those of the upper storey can reach it by means of the hole in the floor. Magnificent foresight on the part of the mechanism of the dessication! The mother Kermes, of whom no more is left than an unsubstantial ceiling, contrives in her substance a trap-door without which half her family would die imprisoned.

Owing to its minute proportions, the tiny insect all but escapes the unaided eye. A good magnifying-glass shows it as a tiny Louse, shaped like an egg, the large end of the egg to the fore, and in colour a delicate reddish brown. It has six very active legs. Its motionless future, its lifeless maturity, are prefaced by a quick, toddling walk. The long antennæ are in constant vibration; on the hinder part of the body are two long, diaphanous cirri, which will escape remark unless we look for them with sustained attention. There are two black eye-spots.

In the small glass test-tube in which I am observing it, the tiny creature appears to be extremely busy. It strays hither and thither, the antennæ outspread and waving to and fro; it climbs, descends, and climbs again, wandering this way and that, colliding as it goes with the torn skins of the hatched eggs. It is making ready for departure, that is evident. This mere speck of life is about to adventure into the wide world. What does it want? Apparently a sprig of its food plant. I have had an eye to its requirements.

In the orchard is an evergreen oak, one single specimen, a small but sturdy tree some ten to twelve feet in height. About the middle of June, when the young are beginning to appear, I place there some thirty Kermes, still adhering to their supporting twig.

In spite of all my pains, it will be no easy matter to follow the peregrinations of the Kermes' family, should it disperse itself over the tree, as I suppose it will. The traveller is too small and the country to be explored too vast. Moreover, to examine the tips of all the boughs with the magnifying-glass, leaf by leaf, twig by twig, is impracticable; no one's patience would suffice to the task.

A few days later I inspect those that are within my range. Many migrations have taken place, as is proved by the white filmy skins left by the roadside. As for the young, I cannot see them anywhere, neither on the bark of the twigs, nor on the leaves. Is it possible that they have all attained the inaccessible tips of the boughs? Or can they have gone elsewhere? This is the first problem to be solved, and it must be solved under such conditions that the emigrants cannot escape my gaze.

I transplant some young evergreen oaks ten to twenty inches in height, into flowerpots filled with leaf-mould. On the twigs of each young tree I fix, with a little drop of gum, five or six Kermes, taking especial care not to obstruct the door of emergence. This miniature artificial coppice is placed where it is sheltered from the fiercest heat of the sun, in my study, facing one of the windows.

On the 2nd of July I witness a migration. At the hottest time of the day, about two o'clock, the new-born Lice leave their fortress in an innumerable swarm. The young Kermes emerge hastily from the door of their dwelling, the button-hole-shaped cleft; many of them dragging behind them the discarded husk of the egg. For a moment they stand motionless on the domed roof of their spherical house; then they scatter over the neighbouring twigs. Several of them climb upwards and reach the summit of the plant, without appearing to gain much satisfaction from their ascent; some of them climb downwards along their twig, so that I cannot possibly guess what objective the swarm is seeking. It may be that we are witnessing a brief period of disorder, due to the joy of the first few steps in a world of unrestricted freedom; the tiny creatures may be wandering at random, abandoned to the delights of emancipation. Let them do as they will; they will soon quiet down.

On the following day, indeed, I can no longer see a single Louse on the tree; all have found their way downwards to the black leaf-mould in the flowerpot, not far from the main stem. This mould, recently watered, is rich in the savours of foliage which has rotted and fallen into dust. There, on a surface barely larger than one's fingernail, the little creatures have gathered into a closely packed flock. Not one of them moves, so well satisfied do they seem with their pasture, or rather their watering-place. As far as I can see they are feeding, motionless in their well-being.

I do what I can to increase their felicity. To keep the place cool and to provide a little shadow I cover it with a few dead leaves from the evergreen oak, previously moistened in a glass of water. And now, little Lice, you must proceed after your own fashion; I have done for you all that I can!

I have just learned of one essential point of your history, one detail, without which all the rest of my investigations must inevitably have come to naught. My first conjectures, although perfectly reasonable, were unfounded. Instead of settling down on some twig, as their mother did before them, the young Lice descend to the ground at the foot of their natal tree. There, in the midst of the mosses and dead leaves, they find a shelter offering some degree of coolness, which will nourish them with its exudations, at all events at the outset.

And what do they live upon later?—I am not in a position to say. For five or six days I find them on the same spot, a motionless flock. Not one of them leaves the flock, not one of them descends underground. Then their numbers begin to diminish; little by little they all disappear, evaporating as it were, returning to that nothingness from which they were so little removed. The flock of atomies has left not a trace.

Apparently the flowerpot with its evergreen oak did not sufficiently fulfil the conditions of prosperity. There should have been also some grasses with underground rootstocks: in short, a jungle of herbaceous vegetation, rich in superficial root-fibres in which the young Kermes would have implanted their suckers. Is this the trouble?

I continue my investigations in the open country, at the foot of some evergreen oaks which, I noted, were thickly populated in May. The families of Lice are certainly there, within a fairly small radius, for the puny little creatures are incapable of a lengthy journey. I inspect the varied vegetation covering the ground beneath the trees; I dig, uproot, and patiently, lens in hand, examine one by one the roots and stems grubbed up. Repeatedly resumed, in winter as well as in autumn, my laborious investigations are fruitless; the tiny Louse cannot be found.

The following year, on the return of spring, I was to learn that the presence of vegetation at the foot of the tree is not a necessity. Let us go back to the evergreen oak in the orchard. I peopled its foliage with some thirty Kermes which had reached maturity. There emerged from it, caravan by caravan, a multitude of Lice. Now, at the foot of this tree and all around it, for a distance of some yards, the soil is perfectly bare. Not a blade of grass, not a weed of any sort, has sprouted on this surface, so recently excavated by the spade. As for the roots of the oak itself, it is, as far as I can judge, useless to take them into account; for they lie at depths which the tiny Louse could never attain.

Yet in May the tree, hitherto exempt from Kermes, is covered with black pills. My sowing has prospered; the young Lice which emerged from the shells have passed the winter underground, and on the advent of warm weather have returned to the tree, there to transform themselves into globules. What did they live on in this ungrateful soil, which contains not a single root-fibre? Probably on nothing at all.

They descend to earth in search of shelter rather than refreshment. Their refuge against the inclemencies of winter is precarious indeed, if it consists, as everything seems to declare, in a few cracks in some lump of earth, not far from the surface. In a hard winter, how many of these ill-protected creatures must disappear? To the ravages of the devourers of new-laid eggs we must add the more dreadful depredations of winter; and thus it is that in order to preserve one life the Kermes gives birth to thousands upon thousands.

The remainder of its story is not easily discovered. It is now the beginning of April. My three children, the joy of my declining years, lend me the keen sight of youth. Without their assistance I should abandon all thought of the chase, which I now propose to pursue on the confines of invisibility. The previous year certain thickets of evergreen oak, well within the reach of the observer, were marked down as being thickly peopled by the Kermes. At that time I marked every populated twig with a white thread.

It is here that my little collaborators patiently pursue their investigations, leaf by leaf, and twig by twig. After a brief glimpse through my lens the harvest is placed in a botanist's specimen box; a more scrupulous examination will be made in my study, with all the conveniences which the observer may require.

On the seventh of April, just as I am beginning to despair of my investigations, the tiny insect crosses the field of my pocket microscope. This is she, actually this is she! Just as I saw her last year emerging from her natal shell, so once more I behold her now. No change whatever is visible: neither of aspect, nor shape, nor colouration, nor size. She goes bustling along as though busy in the extreme, searching doubtless for a spot to her liking. At every moment the smallest wrinkle in the bark conceals her from sight. I place the twig that bears the precious atomy under a bell-glass. On the following day I expect a moult. The bustling little insect is replaced by a motionless corpuscle. This is the first stage of the globular Kermes. Fortune has only once vouchsafed me such a "find," which would have been examined in greater detail had I possessed a sufficient number of subjects. My inspection of the evergreen oaks was somewhat in arrears; I ought to have made it in March. At this period, I imagine, I should have caught the insect emerging from the soil and returning to the foliage of its oak-tree, in order there to undergo transformation. Instead of one single subject I should have had many, though even then I could not have counted upon a numerous collection, for the hardships of winter have certainly thinned out those families, which were in the beginning so numerous. They descended from the tree in their hundreds of thousands; they climb it again in scanty groups, as is attested by the scarcity of the black globules in the warm weather.

As for what becomes of the climbers, my single specimen tells us plainly enough. It has become a spherical speck, the indubitable sign of the future Kermes. In a few days' time it has dried up, despite the glass of water into which the base of the twig was immersed. Fortunately I have a few other similar corpuscles, a little more developed. My gleanings give me two kinds of corpuscle.

The more numerous are spherical in shape, their size varying according to their age. The smallest are rarely a millimetre2 in diameter. The ventral surface is flat, and surrounded by a snowy cushion, the rough foundation of the waxy base. The dorsal surface is rounded, and in colour of a rusty red or pale chestnut with delicate white tufts distributed without any orderly arrangement. In this costume the young Kermes reminds us of a certain shell found in tropical seas: the striped or tiger cowry. The sugar refinery is already at work. At the back of the shell a limpid drop is gathering, to which the Ants repair in order to quench their thirst. In a few weeks' time the colour has changed to an ebony black, the sphere has attained the size of a pea and the Kermes has reached its final state.

The minority stretch themselves out in the likeness of a tiny half-contracted slug. The ventral surface is flat and its whole area is closely applied to the twig. The dorsal surface is convex, and its colour a more or less vivid amber yellow. It is sprinkled with protuberant specks of a snowy white, arranged in longitudinal rows to the number of five or seven. With its amber yellow colouration and its ornamentation of white specks, the tiny creature has something of the look of a certain kind of pastry which is sprinkled with spots of white sugar. There is no oozing of a syrupy liquid to the rear of the insect, so that the Ants do not visit it.

I have conjectured that this second form is the larval state of the males. From this, I imagine, will emerge winged insects ready for mating. To verify this guess of mine is impossible. My slug-like specimens die on their withering twig, and to follow their development beyond the walls of my study would be an undertaking too great for my patience.

Of this very incomplete history of the Kermes of the oak-tree, one point especially should be remembered. The mother, an enormous ovary, exempt from the labours of egg-laying, contracts into a strong-box in which the family is hatched without the removal of the eggs. Within this shrivelled relic the family swarms in its thousands until the moment of exodus. Simplifying to the very extreme the usual method of procreation, the insect turns into a boxful of young.

1 *Kermes* in French, the word is pronounced *Kurmees* in English. The dried bodies of the female insect were long supposed to be galls or berries: they were even known to trade as "kermes berries," and were sometimes used in medicine. It is allied to the cochineal insect, although the female of the latter is very obviously an insect, browsing on the juice of certain cactuses. The kermes is found on several kinds of oak, but principally on the kermes oak, a dwarf evergreen, *Q. Coccifera.—Translator's Note.*

2 Approximately .04 in. or 1/25 in.

INDEX